PATHH – Positive Attitude to Holistic Health
Barbara Chrisp
ISBN: 978-1-9161066-7-3

Living a Yogic life off the mat…

Published by

i2i Publishing. Manchester.
www.i2ipublishing.co.uk

This means taking time to do things that make you truly happy, not the ego-based, fleeting success, but happiness that makes your heart sing and life joyous for you and people around you.

Crafts, music, farming and carpentry are all examples of manual activities, which, just like the Mala beads, support the coordination and connection between the mind, the physical body and the heart. As you hone your chosen skill or skills, you will find purpose and peace as these connections continue to grow.

Your Dharma is yours and yours alone, no one else's will be the same, so open your mind to becoming your unique self.

To perpetuate your 'Bliss', it is important to share your gift, your uniqueness, with others to assist them on their journey. Karma states that what you put out to the universe will return in equal quantity into your life. So, the mutual transfer of positive energy between two souls will give you vitality and strength to continue to thrive. Share your learning, support others in their journey and you will find true happiness.

This is where your true path begins, remember that you are below no one, and be humble enough to accept that you are also above no one. We are all the same but unique in our Soul journey. Celebrate and expand your uniqueness while using it to support others. You are on your journey.

The practice of yoga is not the path so much as the path to your path.

Dear Reader

Life is joy. You truly are the captain of your own destiny and I hope I have been able to support you in some small way as you embark on your journey to peace and greatness.

Every one of us has true greatness within us. We are all filled with unique talents, which, once acknowledged, nurtured and then shared to support others on their journey, will bring back to you a never-ending stream of loving energy.

Discovering my path has changed my life completely, giving me courage to evolve and become the woman I am today. I feel truly blessed that I have had the opportunity to learn and develop these life-changing skills.

Within the past 15 years, my life has gone from high anxiety, confusion and a sense of being set adrift, to strong grounding, purpose and a sense of belonging.

There is true joy to be had in life. Through developing the information offered within this book my world was turned around and has become full of people who feel the same way as I do. We support each other, without expectation or need for acknowledgment. These people are my yogic family and they mean the world to me and I thank them for being them and for being there for me.

Through self-exploration, increasing my understanding of me and changing my outlook in life, my daughter has had freedom to able to grow into a strong woman with an amazing sense of compassion and inner strength. I was also able to open my heart again and now have the kindest and most loving partner who is my true soul mate, my secure port in all storms and the wind beneath my wings as I move forward.

About the Author

 Barbara Chrisp began practicing yoga over 20 years ago during a very difficult time in her life, work was very stressful in the banking sector with business targets of over £10 million per month. She was a single parent of a two-year old, working long hours when her mum was diagnosed with a brain tumor. Life became a blur.

She took up a yoga class to give her a little 'me' time, to feel normal and calm again for just an hour or two per week. However, over the next 10 years, it became her lifeline and gave her strength to continue each day. She learnt how to control her emotional swings and used yogic philosophy to ground and then strengthen her resolve and focus.

After a 10 year battle her mum passed away and she decided to change that painful life lesson into a positive and began training as a yoga teacher to help others who were struggling with life, as she had.

Barbara Chrisp has been teaching since 2011 and offers support and guidance through yoga classes, workshops and retreats within her local community in East Durham.

You can find her on Facebook at Sensesyoga

Introduction to PATHH - The Program

Positive Attitude to Holistic Health

Yogic-based philosophy has supported mankind for thousands of years: it offers guidance in all aspects of life, enabling you to maintain a naturally healthy body, mind and heart. Over the past seven years, I have been teaching programmes using my yogic training to support and guide people back to health. I have created this book to encourage and support those seeking positive change in their lives, and to reassure them that it can be done.

In 2018 a formal evaluation was completed on the benefits of my yogic-based educational programmes, to illustrate and celebrate the diverse richness and most importantly the enduring relevance yogic learning has in a modern, fast paced society. By using NHS-based evaluation tools, I was able to provide strong evidence which is acceptable to health care professionals as well as the general public.

I have outlined below the pilot and its results to demonstrate the kind of benefits you too may experience in your own life and the additional health improvements you may not have thought of from following the teachings of yogic philosophy. The contents of the book offers insight into the areas discussed during the PATHH program and will hopefully support you in your journey.

6

The Pilot

Positive Attitude to Holistic Health (PATHH) programmes change lives through acceptance, awareness and the developed ability to change. The programme uses yogic based philosophy and practice to support the rebalance of the mind, emotions and physical body. Every person who embarks on PATHH does so for their own reasons and each person gets something different out of it. However, the common thread is that they feel better as a result of it.

It is important to acknowledge the fundamental principle of the programme:

'Yoga does not care about the person you have been. Yoga cares about the person you are becoming".

It is therefore important not to dwell on the past, after all, we cannot change what has happened. Instead, we look forward and allow past experiences (or life lessons) to naturally unfold and resolve in their own time.

When you embark on PATHH it is important to establish house rules, to set a balanced playing field so, each person is asked to agree to the following:

I agree that every person is unique and should be celebrated as such, while recognising we are all fundamentally the same: we all have the same fears, worries and need to be accepted and loved.

I give myself permission to be open and honest.

I only use positive language.

I respect each person the way I would like to be respected.

I acknowledge others' points of views without judgement or prejudice.

I leave physical, mental or emotional labels at the door.

I open my mind to new ideas and practices.

It may be helpful for you to establish your house rules, so that you can start with a clean slate.

To highlight the impact of PATHH and the benefits of a 'yogic family', it is best to hear it from someone who has taken part. This is a letter received from Participant #5 of this pilot in March 2019. This person had not missed a single week since the commencement of her journey and was one of the most challenged participants, but also, it turned out, one of the most triumphant. The progress in terms of evaluation results are also shown after the letter.

"It is now six months since the end of the PATHH program, I have continued to use things learnt in those initial six weeks in my everyday life. It's not until now that I look back at the start that I realise how far I have come, it's not the big things, but lots of little things and how they come together that have a knock-on effect which makes the big changes.

I feel I am a different person, happier, more confident and able to cope better with everyday life.

I continue the belly breathing regularly throughout my waking hours, often now without thinking about it. Being able to control my breathing has helped me deal with, and at times stop my panic attacks, palpitations and general fear of living everyday life.

I now try to view life from a positive perception, accept things, and try to see things from more than just one point of view. Everything we do in our lives we do, because at that moment of time it was the right choice, so I think about it and learn from that thought.

I feel I have more courage and I remember to stand tall "I am a mountain". I lift my head up and have eye contact. The more I do this the more I feel I want to do it and my confidence improves.

I feel more relaxed and confident so I find I stutter less, because the words don't get stuck, I find I talk more, I have and can share my thoughts and I now have a point of view, a voice. The stronger, more confident and more in control I feel, helps calm the fear and hyper alertness, so I don't seem to get as upset and end up in a heap of tears, or panic and have to get away.

The pain in my back, shoulders and hips is not as bad as was, as my body is not so tense all the time. When my body does feel tense I breath and work on some of my yoga movements and that helps me focus and settle myself down.

All of these individual things that I learnt and continue to practice come together and have given me a life, it's in colour, not a black existence and although yes, I have bad days, and hiccups, I sit down and think and learn from them, then stand and start again with a clean slate.

The one thing that I aim for and I look forward to all week is a Thursday evening at six when I walk into yoga class and take my place, on my mat, with my friends. I am genuinely welcomed and get smiled at, I chat and listen, I am part of something. It's the one place and time of my week I don't feel so alone, I feel, I belong. I am accepted as me, with all my hang-ups, fears and oddities. I'm not a freak, or a failure if I can't do something, I give it a try and to the group my best is good enough. I keep trying and I will improve and have. It's the one thing in the week I do because I want to, it not my duty or my job or because I have to, by eight I am shattered but happy, content and at peace. I have been through the project with these people I see now as my friends, we all attend for a reason, our own reasons. Every person in that room comes along and tries, no matter what's going on in their heads or their lives, they keep living, keep going, keep taking another step forward along the path of life.

We laugh together, encourage each other, and gain strength from each other, it special. We are guided, helped through, picked up, encouraged, supported and shown how and given strength by a special person, who took us on this journey, and is still there with us. Thankyou Barbara for being you, for believing you can and do make a difference.

Thank you, for showing me and giving me the tools to live a life that isn't any more just an existence."

	Week 1	Week 12	9 Months on
Loneliness rated	36 Extreme	29 Moderate	17 Normal
Anxiety rated	16 Abnormal	10 Borderline (H)	8 Borderline (L)
Depression rated	13 Abnormal	7 Normal	4 Normal
PHQ-9 rated	11 Moderate	10 Moderate	1 Minimal/none

PATHH offered, and still does, an alternative solution and thought process to traditional GP services and provides sustainable improvements to overall health and wellbeing. At the end of 2017, I engaged with a local GP Patient Participant Forum and suggested a program of holistic activities to improve the health and wellbeing of patients within my local area of East Durham in England.

PATHH was initially aimed at adults with poor long term emotional and/or physical health issues which were affecting their ability to go to work, enjoy a full life and maintain relationships with family and friends; which led to many of them becoming socially isolated and in most cases also have symptoms of poor mental health. In every instance, each participant said they felt as though they were at a crisis point and like they were running out of options or that nothing was going to help them 'get better'. The purpose of the pilot was to evaluate whether holistic health activities such as mindfulness, yogic philosophy and yoga practice could improve health outcomes of the participants.

Participant #19 states as of March 2019

"I embarked on this journey last year with some trepidation I must admit, not knowing exactly what I was getting into, and I could not see anything positive in my life at that time.

I was at a really low point in my life I was willing to try a completely new avenue.

My physical health had a huge impact on my emotional and spiritual wellbeing. My first meeting with PATHH was informative and very emotional. I thought I would show myself up, as the emotional wreck I was. However, I very quickly found most of the people in group I was with were just as vulnerable as me.

When I began my journey with PATHH I wasn't convinced it would help, I was on multiple pain killers and anti-depressants.

Today thanks to PATHH and Barbara I no longer need either the pain killers or the anti-depressants, I would recommend this to everyone.

As a society, we have been led to believe medication prescribed by Doctors can cure all ills. When really, we just need to listen to our bodies, as PATHH has given us the ability to do. We can help our bodies and minds cure ourselves."

Starting blood pressure reading   114/70

Finishing blood pressure reading   130/80

GP referral form (June 18) states;

Was awaiting investigative surgery for ongoing stomach problems

GP feedback after PATHH (Oct 18) states;

'tummy' problems have gone. Really made a difference. Outlook completely changed.

Also lost weight.

April 2019 - Participant #9 has now been off anti-depressants for almost six months and no longer required investigation for stomach problems as they have not returned.

Program Content

The PATHH program is 12 weeks long and is aligned to the 'mental health pathways' habit-changing guidelines to support the development of new, sustainable processes through the following objectives:

To develop the foundations of being present and aware.

To develop life skills to support ongoing health improvement.

To take part in a mixture of theory and practical activities which develops an understanding of why and how negative stress develops in the body and what can be done to reduce it.

To understand the physical, mental and emotional effects stress has on day to day living; and to firstly identify, then manage individual triggers.

To explore coping mechanisms and techniques to reduce the negative effects of stress; and build resilience.

Explore the benefits of low impact, gentle yogic movement on the physical and mental body.

To appreciate the importance of completing tasks to build resilience in life through structured practice. Following everything through to its natural conclusion.

To enhance the use of breathing techniques to create a sense of calm and focus within the mind and heart so reducing stress and anxiety.

In addition, participants also experience…

Two-week Introduction to Yoga

Participants were introduced to the practice of yoga with particular focus on gentle release of physical tension, the building of strength, posture and movement through the body to elevate pain and discomfort while developing a sense of all-round health and wellbeing. They experienced how yoga builds a sense of calm within the body and mind through working them in harmony and using the breathing techniques during practice. The adaptability of yoga makes it suitable for any age or ability and everyone was able to fully participate with correct tuition.

Two-week Introduction to Relaxation and Meditation

Using the principle of Yin and Yang participants experience the importance of structured relaxation and concentration to bring balance to their day. The participants practiced calming and focusing breathing techniques to help reduce the effects of negative stress, anxiety and sleep problems through Pranayama based practices. Participants continued to develop their 'breathing space' and learned simple concentration practices and techniques to build up focus and resilience to difficult situations in their lives

Two-week Introduction to Chi Kung (or QI Gong)

Participants were introduced to the practice of Chi Kung which is a soft form of Tai Chi, with particular focus on the Chinese self-healing techniques. Chi Kung supports the development of healthy cell growth within the body to improve energy and strength through focused breath, movement and a positive, calm mindset. The adaptability of Chi Kung makes it suitable for any age or ability.

The health issues of the people taking part ranged from chronic pain due to long term health issues, recovering from cancer, bereavement and abuse, to general loss of confidence and self-esteem. Most participants demonstrated high levels of anxiety, depression and loneliness and most participants said they didn't expect the programme to work and that they had tried many things over the years, which either hadn't made a difference or only made a difference in the short term. The participants also talked about feelings of desperation and nearly all of them said their biggest fear about taking part in PATHH was that it wouldn't work and that how they felt at the starting point was going to be how they feel for the rest of their lives. Most had lost hope.

The evaluation documents used were the UCLA Loneliness Scale, which is a commonly used measure of loneliness, Hospital Anxiety and Depression Scale (HADS) for anxiety and depression at the beginning and end of the program. All the participants demonstrated an improvement in one or more outcome area and from a programme perspective it's clear to see the overall impact of PATHH as all participants moved towards 'normal' ranges of loneliness, depression and anxiety as a result of taking part in the 12-week programme. This was significant in that many of them had reported having depression and anxiety for a prolonged period of time, sometimes years and had tried other interventions and medical treatments which they felt had failed to make a difference.

UCLA Loneliness Scale Results

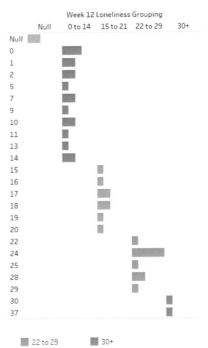

Week 1 Loneliness Table

Wk 1 Loneliness Grouping	%	No of Clients
0 to 14	23%	9
15 to 21	15%	6
22 to 29	31%	12
30 +	31%	12
Grand Total	100%	39

Week 12 Loneliness Table

Week 12 Loneliness Grouping	% of Clients	No of Clients
Null	5%	2
0 to 14	44%	17
15 to 21	21%	8
22 to 29	26%	10
30+	5%	2
Grand Total	100%	39

HADS Anxiety Results

Null
1 to 7
8 to 10
11 to 20

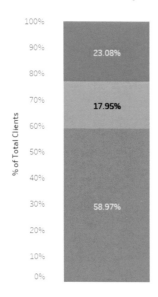

Week 1 HADS Anxiety

23.08%

17.95%

58.97%

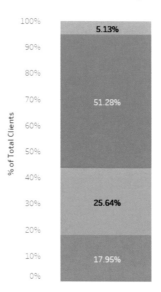

Week 12 HADS Anxiety

5.13%

51.28%

25.64%

17.95%

Week 1 HADS Anxiety Table

Wk 1 Anxiety Category	Wk 1 Anxiety Score	%	No of Clients
Normal	0 to 7	23%	9
Borderline	8 to 10	18%	7
Abnormal	11 to 20	59%	23
Grand Total		100%	39

Week 12 HADS Anxiety Table

Wk 12 Anxiety Category	Wk 12 Anxiety Score	%	No of Clients
Null	Null	5%	2
Normal	1 to 7	51%	20
Borderline	8 to 10	26%	10
Abnormal	11 to 20	18%	7
Grand Total		100%	39

HADS Depression Results

Week 1 (No of clients by group)   Week 12 (No of clients by group)

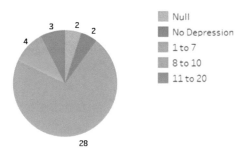

Week 1 HADS Depression Table

Week 1 Category	Wk 1 Score	%	No of Clients
Normal	No Depression	3%	1
	1 to 7	36%	14
Borderline	8 to 10	26%	10
Abnormal	11 to 21	36%	14
Grand Total		100%	39

Week 12 HADS Depression Table

Wk 12 Category	Wk 12 Score	%	No of Clients
Null	Null	5%	2
Normal	No Depression	5%	2
	1 to 7	72%	28
Borderline	8 to 10	10%	4
Abnormal	11 to 20	8%	3
Grand Total		100%	39

Willingness to Change

As part of our evaluation it was important to monitor how participants' confidence in their ability to self-heal improved and also, whether their level of scepticism decreased. We asked them to complete a quiz on week one and week twelve to establish their perception of being able to improve their health by thought, awareness and positive actions. The quiz evaluated the participants level of personal responsibility and accountability for their own health and wellbeing. All but two participants increased their final score indicating a higher level of personal empowerment to change.

Week 1 - Willingness to change Table

		%	No of Clients
Null	No data supplied	10%	4
0 to 10	Believes body cannot change and holistic health is unlikely to make any physical change	21%	8
11 to 20	Is open to change and has broadened ideas about self-healing	69%	27
Grand Total		100%	39

Week 12 - Willingness to Change Table

		%	No of Clients
Null	No data supplied	5%	2
0 to 10	Believes body cannot change and holistic health is unlikely to make any physical change	3%	1
11 to 20	Is open to change and has broadened ideas about self-healing	85%	33
20+	Firmly accepts alternative therapies as a method of healing	8%	3
Grand Total		100%	39

Nine Months On

Since finishing PATHH in October 2018 additional yoga classes were set up to maintain support for the participants in their journey.

Those who continued their practice were asked to complete the same evaluation as done at week one and 12 of the formal PATHH, to establish any further benefits they felt by continuing to attend holistic classes and groups.

Attendance at classes were as follows;

Weekly yoga class	18 participants per week
Meditation	10 participants per week
Chi Kung	4 participants per week
Craft group	6 participants fortnightly
workshops	7 participants monthly
Yoga Retreats	4 participants

Loneliness Scale

Loneliness scale			
	extreme	moderate	normal
week 1	5	7	5
9 months on	1	4	12

Nine months on, only one person stated that they felt extremely lonely, while 12 rated themselves within normal range.

To leave labels at the door and become a 'family' has supported the participants in their journey to feel part of a community, the yoga family. The desire for family and community is a basic human need and when we reduce our loneliness, we experience less fear and fewer emotional swings (as indicated below).

HADS Anxiety Scale

HADS - Anxiety			
	abnormal	borderline	normal
week 1	11	3	3
9 months on	3	2	12

16 out of 17 participants saw a reduction in their levels of anxiety.

We started with a staggering 11 of the 18 participants rating themselves with extreme anxiety and only two as normal. At the final evaluation 12 participants rating themselves as normal and only three abnormal. This was the biggest banding change within the evaluation, which indicated a huge reduction in their sense of stress and fear in life. This came from establishing a practice physical health improvement along with a sense of calm and acceptance, which in turn develops courage and resilience.

HADS Depression Scale

HADS - Depression			
	abnormal	borderline	normal
week 1	7	5	6
9 months on	1	3	**13**

15 out of 17 participants saw a reduction in their experiences of depression, with 7 extreme ratings reducing to 1, and the normal rating more than doubled. This has enabled a reduction or ceasing of anti-depressants for many participants. Participants said they felt happier because they were more in control of their bodies, minds and future. They also noted that other people saw a difference in them and that they were proud of their achievements.

Participant comments and feedback after 12 weeks

"I've gone through life not knowing how to breathe properly. When I feel the stress or chaos rising, I take a few moments out and just breathe."

"I worry less and enjoy life more. I feel less stressed and feel more grateful."

"I would recommend the PATHH programme to anyone suffering with anxiety/depression it really does help to change/save your life. I now can say I don't feel like I have any negative words in my vocabulary which is a huge difference to how I felt 12 weeks ago."

"Hearing other peoples' stories has made me realise they struggle with some things that I take for granted, and it makes me feel more fortunate and grateful"

"Instead of wasting energy worrying about situations beyond my control, I am trying to accept situations as is, and not let it affect my emotions negatively"

"I am returning to work on 17th Sept, my managers have commented on how well I am doing and how far I have come and that it's lovely to see me getting back to my old self. I am looking forward to getting back to work which is something I thought I would never say"

"Negative emotional words are no longer in my vocabulary"

"I have recently handled/coped with a situation using mindfulness techniques that I have learnt during the course. I would normally have got angry and dealt with things badly."

"It is empowering to know I can control my reactions and feelings in situations, although I know this is just the beginning and I have a way to go, but looking forward to the journey"

"To begin with I was surprised at how openly emotional I was. I felt quite vulnerable and very overwhelmed. However, I was shocked at how quickly I became comfortable within the group and how well we bonded"

"I was surprised at my determination to see the course through in the belief that it will help me. I now go for a 20-25-minute walk most days and have cut down on my alcohol consumption. I attribute this not just

to the fact that the course makes you aware you should look after yourself but also that if someone is prepared to invest in your wellbeing that you should too!"

Comments from continued PATHH participants March 2019

"PATHH changed my life, in fact it helped to give me my life back when life was the last thing I wanted"

"I have finished my degree after 20yrs, through motivation and 'finishing' ethics of yoga practice. I am now starting my MA in Design, returning to my roots of creative practice for my own self-nourishment and am developing my Art Therapy business idea."

"I feel stronger, more confident with less low moods. I am more grounded. There is a great sense of "yoga family" connection and support"

"Friends comment on the new me and how they love it!'

"My husband said he feels he is now able to show me he cares. He felt I closed him out before PATHH"

"I am no longer less of a person after cancer, I am more of one!"

"I have taken on a vegan way of living and over the past nine months have lost just over two stone in weight. I feel happy, confident and really well"

Four Examples of Reduced Medical Intervention

"I started the program taking three Fluoxatine and two Propanalol. I am now down to two tablets in total each day.

"I take FLUXETINE for depression, which I have taken on and off for 30 years. I was taking 3x20mg capsules daily, but for the last three months this has reduced to 2x20mg capsules and I am coping no problem. I hope to continue to reduce it further."

*"I used to be on 4mg of Warfarin but since starting PATHH I have been able to come off it and as a result of this, in March 2019 I had my **pacemaker removed**. I had also had a stroke which left me very weak on my left side. I am getting much stronger and my balance is also much better.*

"I am no longer showing symptoms of Crohn's disease and so no investigation or medication has needed to be prescribed"

The PATHH pilot has provide strong evidence that yogic-based holistic health programmes are very effective and can make a huge impact on people's lives.

There will always be a need for medical intervention for physical ailments and conditions, however, using holistic support alongside medical services, individuals can become more empowered to improve their mental and emotional stability, strength and resilience in everyday life, without being labelled or expected to explain themselves.

Just over half of the starting numbers have continued with yogic practice, expanding out to other groups and increasing their knowledge and therefore their understanding of themselves.

There are also participants who now feel so passionate about yoga and yogic philosophy that they are starting a journey to become a teacher too, to pass on their experience and help others. This is the yogic way.

Many participants have reduced or stopped the need for medication during the programme or have had medical tests or investigations halted as their symptoms have gone.

The feedback received from non-continuing participants is that they feel they now have the tools to proactively work through situations in life and are happy in the knowledge that they can come back to a class if or when they feel they want/need to.

Many of the participants have remained in touch and several people have returned to full time employment after being on extended sick from work, while others have started new jobs.

PATHH enables people to make gentle changes to their lives to make them better, but the most prominent area identified is having the knowledge that ongoing support is available if or when needed. Longevity of holistic support gives people time to expand and become stronger and having security that there is someone there for them has a huge positive impact on confidence. This has been shown in the second review where participants' sense of loneliness dropped significantly from the beginning the pilot. This also echoes in the reduction of anxiety as participants said they felt they could relax, knowing they were not alone: they have a yoga family.

As a closing comment, I would like to say that Yoga is not a magic pill and the results above should not be taken for granted, they were achieved through hard work and a determination to change. They are ordinary people, with everyday struggles and issues trying to keep afloat and keep going. They eventually understood that perfection is impossible, however, doing your best, with good intentions is achievable every day. That is good enough.

The participants need to be recognised, and their achievements acknowledged as evidence of the sheer potential that human nature has, and the greatness people can achieve when given support and gentle guidance. I am very proud of them all.

The participants have shown great courage, compassion for others within their group and strength of personal character in their journey so far. They have found their feet and their standing in their family and community. They have found their voice.

I intend be able to continue to see them grow and expand and watch them flourish over the coming years.

PATHH is the participants, PATHH can be you too.

Dear Reader,

Thank you for investing in your journey back to your true self, in your PATHH.

Within this book you will find tools and support to help you first find your roots and then your wings, which can often be described as your purpose in life. I invite you to use this book as your personal journal; write in it, scribble in it, stick bits into it. Use it to help you document your learning and development. This journey will, at times, be challenging. It will require personal reflection, acceptance and commitment. Remember the easiest path is not always the right one for you and your personal development, so take time to acknowledge that you are investing in yourself and that it is you who will ultimately reap the benefits of this effort when challenges occur.

Read the book through once and then go back, taking your time - weeks, months even - in each section. Always bear in mind that everything positive in your life has a purpose and every setback or hurdle provides a lesson to be learned. Make sure you use every positive influence and learn from every setback as you move through this journey.

As I developed my own personal understanding, my life became simpler but at the same time was endowed with much more meaning. I was able to let go of the baggage I had been carrying around in life as I began to listen to my heart and recognize my true self. I realized that all the external successes in life mean nothing unless you have success within, in your heart and soul. I now feel younger, lighter and full of energy every day, taking great joy in the little things.

Connecting with yourself is a magical experience and once achieved creates personal greatness and strength in life. To be mindful is to be conscious and aware, accepting situations without judgment, living in the moment rather than sifting through past events or setting up emotional barriers that may block future potential growth. Take time to get to know yourself, by spending time alone, without distractions. When you spend time investing in yourself, you begin to connect with your heart and find peace in life. So, commit your learning to the discovery of your true heart as it will never lie to you or set you up to fail. Your heart frees you from the rat race and the ego, and you will be truly successful in life when you live through love.

Good luck on your journey.

What is Mindfulness?

The book is a culmination of my personal yogic learning over the past 20 years. As well as traditional Hatha and Kriya yoga, the foundation of my practice is based upon a combination of Raja yoga and the Eight-Limbed Path of Patanjali, which has offered me guidance to a more meaningful and peaceful existence. In addition, the book also contains aspects of my personal learning from many other sources, which have supported my spiritual development, created a sense of grounding in my life and formed the basis for PATHH.

In order to support your learning, I suggest that you engage with a good yoga teacher, who resonates with you and your learning needs at this time in your life and will enable you to have practical face to face support each week. This will help you move forward safely and with more confidence.

You can find a million and one books on 'Mindfulness' and how to achieve it. Mindfulness is simply the practice of being in the present moment and being truly aware of your surroundings without emotional influence. This in turn enables proactive decision making to take place and improve the positive flow of energy within the body. Modern living habits mean we spend so much of our time on AUTO-PILOT, due to excessive emotional influences like anxiety, stress or depression, to name just a few, that we spend the whole day doing things without thinking about them or paying attention. You could call this 'Mind-full' living, creating a reactionary and impulsive way of living.

The Seven Principles of Mindfulness

To support mindful living, there are seven aspects to consider, understand and then weave into your daily life. They will not be achieved overnight or in a matter of weeks, these principles grow over months and years with gentle daily consideration.

Letting go – of emotional attachments, whether they are good or bad, so you don't get caught up in 'perceived' experiences.

Acceptance – of yourself as an individual, your role in society and the world around you

Non-judging – the ability to look at each experience as a neutral observer, do not get caught up in other people's experiences.

Beginners Mind – suspend expectations; see each experience as new. Each moment we are alive is unique, a gift.

Patience – do not rush things, instead allow things to unfold naturally.

Non-striving – aim for stillness in the mind to achieve greatness in action.

Trust – in yourself! You are the only person who can truly say what is good and right for you.

These principles will be looked at in more detail throughout the book and support all aspects of yogic living.

Reconnecting

Nature is a wonderful thing and the first step to reconnecting with life and creating a sense of grounding within it, is to develop a heartfelt appreciation for Mother Nature, the natural world, and realise we are a vital part within it. Humans, as the planet's top predator have mostly forgotten that we are no more important nor less important than any other living being - within the flow of the earth, we are all the same. So, it is important to reignite faith in the world around us, revel in the marvels of nature and truly appreciate the complexity and ingeniousness it shows to survive, evolve and thrive in the most challenging of situations.

It is our responsibility to work with the world, and not just people, to ensure the balance is maintained so we can continue to survive. Spend time to consider the following…

Since the beginning of time, every living thing, be it plant, fish or animal, from the smallest amoeba to the mightiest creature, has each lived within the natural order of the world. From the very bottom of the food chain to the very top, each creature knows instinctively how to live and how to live well. Every animal's priority is survival; finding nourishment and water, staying alive long enough to find a mate and continue the gene pool.

Some of nature's wonders live a solitary life, and come together, through one of nature's great miracles, on one single night each year to create new life; gathering in their tens of thousands in a single place to then disappear again. Others thrive on being in family groups, spending their entire lives together in a highly social environment. They support each other, even looking after each other's offspring, and fight to protect the group in times of crisis. There is a natural order to life and a perpetual flow of energy which can be broken down into three elements, the creation of life, the reason for living and, finally, death.

The Creation of Life

The creation of life is Mother Nature's greatest achievement of all. Every living organism on the planet is part of the process of creating new life and perpetuating life energy. It is such a driving force within the primal instinct, the need to pass on genetics, that in some cases creatures can go to such extreme lengths to achieve it that it results in their own death. The transfer of life's vital energy, the creation of new life, whether it is the plants coming into bloom each spring or giving birth to infants, has been explained within scientific world very effectively. However, this transfer of energy should still be greatly appreciated and never taken for granted. Mother Nature, through the process of evolution, has been gently modifying and adapting each living entity on the planet for billions of years, removing and adding to each species to ensure the earths delicate balance is maintained. Mankind should appreciate modern science for its knowledge but importantly stay connected to nature, accept, appreciate and marvel in its work and support all life forms as each are co-dependent of each other. Including us.

The Purpose of Life

It is reassuring to think that every organism created on the planet has a purpose, a reason for being. In the myriad of ecosystems of the natural world, each life supports and protects the delicate and intricate balance of survival. In nature there is balance. In nature nothing is wasted. The bee collects nectar and pollinates the plants, the animals eat the plants and their waste products go back into the soil, providing nutrients that enable the flowers which nourish the bee, perpetuating life. In nature there is symmetry. The soothing dock leaf can be found growing beside the stinging nettle. It's all balance.

There are four things that are needed to survive. Nourishment, water, sun and air. A balanced combination means survival to adulthood, living well and ultimately achieving nature's goal to create new life, continuing to strengthen the gene pool. Visualize life as a battery, continuously recharging and being drawn down, extracting and storing as much natural energy from the food consumed, the water drank, light absorbed and the air breathed, to create an explosion of life. However, if there is a deficiency in one or more of these areas, there cannot be enough energy to achieve the purpose of continuation.

Yogic thinking takes this one step further, it looks at each living organism as a soul with a life lesson to be learned. Each soul is born into a form to experience, connect, and grow. For the soul to evolve it also needs positive interaction with other souls.

To live well, humans, like all other living beings need to live their lives according to their lesson, and need the connection with others to learn and achieve their reason for being. They need to belong. When you have a sense of community you can thrive in that purpose as you are constantly positively connecting, creating energy for life, learning and improving yours and others lives. It therefore follows that the opposite applies, when you disrespect and disrupt your homelife and surroundings you are actually disrespecting and disrupting yourself and you are damaging your own sense of belonging and personal energy.

From a yogic view, it is therefore vital for the longevity of the heart and soul and to be able to live life well to maintain that sense of community, a sense of positive connection to others. This is achieved by embracing our individual unique qualities while acknowledging we are all fundamentally the same, a soul on a journey with the need to belong, cooperate with others and learn their lesson by communicating well. By creating a sense of belonging and inclusiveness in society through respect within and outside the home the heart becomes peaceful, without fear, and it can open and expend, giving you the courage to live life to its fullest potential. It supports the completion of your purpose in life and allows the soul to expand and travel well.

Death

All good things must come to an end. Or must they? Phrases like 'the circle or life', 'where you find death you find life' and others, all hint that there is a constant ebb and flow within the energy on our planet.

Life begins with a huge injection of energy, fully charging the battery. During the time given to live there is a need for daily recharging, keeping the battery topped up through the absorption of energy from the four vital forces. Once new life has been created, the battery begins to be less effective and energy levels begin to fall and are drained more easily until the point where it fails.

When the vital force leaves the physical frame, death occurs. This is the same throughout nature: from leaves losing their green glow, shriveling to brown and dropping off the tree in winter, to the mighty elephant who removes itself from the herd and goes off to die; nature has given signals which must be obeyed. Everything has a finite time for existence, and this is accepted as the natural order of life. We are part of nature, and part of this natural order of birth, living and death.

However, this death only applies to the physical shell that holds perpetual life energy.

Many religions and philosophies going back to the earliest civilizations have understood the concept of 'Energy' or the 'Soul'. Energy *is* the soul, and once the current incarnation, be it animal, human, bird, fish is spent, the vital force or energy leaves the vessel and the soul moves on.

Death can be viewed as the end of a chapter, with a new one to begin, a new experience to be had. The earliest civilizations believed, and so have many civilizations since, that life is part of a never-ending cycle of energy. As the battery fails, the energy simply moves to the next physical casing, ready to start again. This is what we know as rebirth or reincarnation.

So where did we go wrong?

It is quite often said that man was the monkey that got lucky. Perhaps it was a stronger will to survive, which helped to develop the mind and give humans the ability to create fire and hunting tools, enabling us to climb to the very top of the food chain.

The primal brain is the body's inbuilt survival mechanism and is still active within the mind today. Striving to become safer in its environment, assessing and evaluating every situation for potential threats and danger. The primal brain, quite often known as the reptilian complex, is your very own health and safety manager. Over thousands of years of development, man has eliminated all his natural predators as he gradually honed his survival skills, began working in hunting groups, and discovered the use of weapons and then warfare strategies to eliminate all of his perceived threats.

Groups became larger for safety and hierarchies developed, individual skills enhanced and roles within the groups settled, males became the hunter gatherers (though it is well documented that in some cultures women fought alongside men) while females developed nurturing and community skills. We began to develop the neocortex, our centre of reason within the brain.

Modern man has discovered many ancient civilizations during their quest for knowledge and we now know a huge amount about Mayans, ancient Egyptians, ancient Greeks and ancient Romans to name a few. We have even found cave drawings in Australia's northern territories dating back 23,000 years. Many of the ancient cultures have a similar thread running through them and that was a respect for nature and their GODS. Many believed that their soul had a journey and when that was over, it would continue to dwell on another level. The foundation for life, to live well, requires us to believe that our life has had meaning and there is something to move onto when the physical body fails. To know there is rewards for the way you have lived your life creates focus and commitment in the current one.

An example of this is the Vikings who were the most fearsome fighters because they believed the greater the warriors they became the more they would be celebrated in Valhalla. Having courage in life and dying by the sword was essential to their onward journey into the next life.

Also, ancient Hindu philosophy (and yogic) believes that each life teaches and completes a specific lesson. If a person has been cruel in this life, they return to experience cruelty in their next life. They can achieve enlightenment by becoming kinder and purer with each lesson learned, or each life lived. As a result of which, passing from one life to the next is usually very peaceful and filled with joy if the person feels that they have completed their life lesson.

Even modern religions such as the Christian church instruct today that if the soul is good then they will be welcomed into heaven, however, if they have been unkind or unjust then, come judgement day, they will be denied entry.

A strong connection with nature has been essential to the progress of mankind; from understanding the seasons and learning when to plant and harvest crops, to building settlements that are both sheltered by and protected from nature's elements. In addition, man's relationship with certain animals has allowed for faster and more efficient advancement, with them assisting in farming and transportation of goods, as well as providing comfort as beloved pets.

Respecting nature, only taking what is needed, having faith that nature will provide, that crops will grow, and the family will thrive has also been integral to the development of mankind.

Humans established their gods to provide an explanation for the inexplicable. The Sun God brings life and grows the crops, the Moon God brings the end of life, creating balance: the beginning and the end. It was believed that each day the sun would rise and set, and the moon would come out. Life begins and must end to allow another period to begin, creating a never-ending cycle.

Every civilization set out rules to live by, rules which generally promoted loyalty and contentment; not to steal from each other, not to kill within their community, etc. All of mankind had a simple, balanced understanding of why they were alive, what was expected of them while they were here and what would happen to them at the end of this life's journey.

Modern man, however, has mostly lost sight of the connection we have with nature. The quest for continuing, externalised knowledge and evolution has sped up to an almost lightening pace. Instead of being content with the mysteries of life and saying, "Oh, I don't know, isn't it wonderful!", we say "Oh! I don't know! Isn't that terrible!".

The need for knowledge has not necessarily brought mankind happiness or contentment, in fact, in most cases it has brought further disconnection from the natural rhythm of life. If mankind no longer believes in the onward journey then he has no purpose in being alive, there is no consequence of not being good or striving to make life more fulfilling and generous to others. The reduction of faith, be it religious or personal beliefs has bred greed, fear and a lack of Soul among many.

The further mankind has looked outward, searching for knowledge and explanations, the less connected and contented with life he has become. As a society, as mankind becomes more externalised in his goals and ambitions, he moves further away from the natural ability to discern whether something is right or wrong, or the ability to listen to the gut instinct and just know. Large scale external referencing creates emotional unrest.

Questions lead to more questions causing a sense of instability in the mind and soul.

When we let go of the 'need to know' we can experience life as it is, in its truest form. Life is full of mysteries and that is what makes it magical, and the ability to accept and thrive in it by having faith in your own judgement is a gift that everyone has been given. Returning to a sense of stability and insight is achievable, even at such a disconnected time as now.

In a busy modern world that has information literally at its fingertips, the constant searching for answers, facts or reasons has created a sense, and sometimes fear, of not knowing. This, in turn, has caused an almost epidemic of depression and anxiety, which manifests itself in the physical form of disease. (Dis-ease, the lack of ease or peace in the body.)

Yogic philosophy dating back over 4,000 years has taught us to listen to our bodies and go with the instinct of the gut and the heart. Ongoing scientific research has proven a connection between the psyche (mind), the immune system (the body), and the nervous system (emotion/soul). They call it Psychoneuroimmunology. Yogis call it mind, body and soul.

Yogic philosophy, and now medical science, state that there is a real connection between the state of mind and the state of health within the body, and that if you are low emotionally it directly effects the immune system and the physical body, just as being physically ill can have a significant negative effect on your mental health.

What you truly believe, you will become.

Physical health and emotional health are linked through the chemicals of consciousness, or neuropeptides, that carry signals to the body from the brain and back again in a constant flow of information.

You know that if you are worried or feeling down, you physically function less effectively; your reaction times are slower, and the physical body starts to feel the emotional pain and so creates a downward spiral of negative emotions – physical discomfort.

In the same way the reverse is true. Physical sensations such as pain, hunger, even a loving embrace can directly affect the emotions, both negatively and positively. However, the connection goes much deeper than this, even affecting us on a cellular level, in the creation of new cells in the body.

It has frequently been observed that if you are positive and happy during a time of illness, your health improves more quickly. This is because the chemicals of consciousness within your body have receptors in the immune system, whose main role is to maintain health and heal the body when damaged. A positive mind helps to heal the body in a positive, healthy and more efficient way.

Conversely, when you are angry and have feelings of, *"Why me!"*, the chemicals of anger flow through the body and attach themselves to your healthy cells, making it difficult to heal, so recovery times are longer and harder. Also, organs such as the liver can be adversely affected by angry emotions, hindering them from functioning properly.

Happy emotions create happy, healthy cells and a strong immune system. It is estimated that there are approximately 86 million neurons within the body, with the largest density of these located within the gut. So, science now supports what yogic philosophy has taught for thousands of years: the gut has a mind. You do have 'gut instinct', so you should listen to it.

Nature has given us a wonderfully intelligent and protective physical body, which works tirelessly every day to keep us well. Even when we abuse it with bad food, alcohol, drugs, smoke and chemicals, and when we neglect it by not allowing it to rest and repair during sleep, forcing it to the limits of endurance, it is still loyal, it still does its utmost to protect you and keep you well.

So, who or what is to blame when it eventually fails? Only you.

As part of your journey to a more peaceful and fulfilling life, take time to consider, with kindness, your lifestyle, the choices you have made so far and intentions you have currently been working to. Instead of searching far and wide, moving further away from yourself in search of answers, justifications and confirmations, start to return home, back to your heart and soul. Enjoy the safety of just being, and begin to look inwards to yourself, physically, emotionally and mentally. Get to know yourself in your truest form and you will learn to appreciate and respect the amazing work your body does and begin to see your true potential.

Open yourself up to start walking your true path in life. Acknowledge that there is always a pathway back to health and happiness. Know that you can find your path. You may not see it yet but allow yourself the comfort, deep down inside, in knowing that you can find your way. You just need to start looking inwards and believing in yourself and your heart.

Place a picture here of you at your happiest in life so far.

Things to think about…

Take some time to look at your life so far, try to determine where your disconnection from your heart started. What were the outside influences? What are your current focuses in life and are you happy with them?

Notes

Fact or faith;

to prove you are right or to just know.

This is one of the most difficult challenges of modern times. Media, parents, teachers and communities are the first point of learning, influence and understanding as a child. They shape thought processes, expectations in life and condition the mind as to how to think, what to believe, and how to feel about the world.

As the infant grows into a youth then adulthood, they develop their own thoughts and learn from personal experiences to develop and evolve through life. With this learning comes the perpetual need to move forward and upwards, constantly searching for the next piece of information or evidence to prove or disprove previous thoughts or revelations. When unchecked and unbalanced, it can cause a shift further from ones true self and personal truth. The wheel stops rolling, the pendulum of yin and yang stops gently swinging. Many people, living in hectic modern society rarely, if ever, listen to their gut instinct or use their own intellect. Instead, they allow themselves to be told or be influenced by others.

FACT - A thing that is known or proven to be.

FAITH - Complete trust or confidence in someone or something.

'Fact' requires external validation from others, known as external referencing. In other words, we need other people to tell us what they know or what they have proven to be true through research and exploration. However, you can have different people look at one piece of evidence or research and they will come up with a different outcome or conclusion. A different slant on their truth.

A thousand years ago it was considered a fact that the world was flat and if you sailed for more than a few days from shore you would most definitely fall off the edge of the world. Now, it is proven to be a fact that the world is round, however, this does not take away the strength of conviction in the original belief at that time in history.

Their knowledge and understanding of their world, was the truth because everyone believed in that truth. Truth is fluid, as what someone has proven to be true can quite often be proven to be untrue by someone else given further information. The facts can very quickly become fiction. An example of which is seen on an almost weekly basis with conflicting facts about the food we eat and what is deemed healthy and what is deemed to be damaging to health.

'Faith' requires only your belief that something is right and good. It is internal referencing at its best, referring only to your personal understanding, your heart and gut reaction for validation of the truth, your personal trust in your own instinct or intuition. As time passes and your understanding and knowledge of a situation improves, your truth may shift and evolve. However, because it has been established from your own experience, your decisions based on your judgement of a situation, your personal conviction and clarity become more powerful and steadfast.

Facts are someone else's interpretation of a situation, with the information they have, therefore, their argument for their truth.

Evidence is a tool to persuade in favor of a point, and that is why in a court room you have two highly trained people who can argue a piece of evidence from two separate directions, for and against the facts presented. English law then requires twelve people of good character and who are unbiased with previous knowledge of a case to evaluate and decide what they believe to be true and the nation have faith that the right decision will be reached. The court service provides 'facts' and the jury provide a judgement by demonstrating their 'faith' in what they have heard, resulting in a balanced, considered decision made with good conscience, usually resulting in the right outcome.

In day to day living, faith or personal conviction is enriching to the soul and allows life lessons to be learned. It allows the mind and heart to evaluate what they believe to be their truth, right here, right now. Faith is the flow of positive energy that has a desire to learn from its own understanding of life and is adaptable to learning experiences, which shape and mould our heart-felt facts, which we have proven to ourselves, what we know to be true. This is human nature at its most unique, we were born to experience and evaluate, and to thrive we must be an active participant in life rather than an observer.

Submitting to someone else telling you their facts is not truly living as you are relying on other people to have the experience for you. You are not really living your life as you are consciously or subconsciously putting your soul into shackles, limiting your life experiences, shortening your outlook and creating fear within your mind and heart. If you believe you are not able to do something, because someone told you so, then your soul will become weaker, your confidence in your own ability shrinks and your life can become a self-imposed prison cell.

Facts are simply pieces of information that someone has experienced. For example, if a scientist has a theory, they may run tests to identify a trend, to prove their research. This is a fact because it is their truth. Use the information wisely, decide what you believe to be true once you have all the information available to you.

'Take that with a pinch of salt' is an old saying where people accept what someone is saying but they add their 'salt', their flavor, their instinctive feel to it too. Information is an important tool for personal growth, listen to what is said, what you read and see. Take it and acknowledge it, however, do not blindly accept it as the only option. Instead, take time to listen to your heart and evaluate if it sits true emotionally. Your gut instinct will give you a reaction of whether the information is good or bad and your mind will be able to gently argue for and against and come up with your truth. This is what human nature has evolved to do.

Use the thousands of years of knowledge and wisdom held in your primal brain, your instinct, and with your centre of reason use empathy to be able to see both sided of the situation, use compassion to love where no love exists, discuss and compromise to be able to co-operate with each other and make life happier and more productive for you and the people living around you.

Facts are information or current/temporary understanding of what is known at this moment in time, either through personal experience or from other people.

Faith is a permanent confidence and trust in your personal ability to see right and wrong.

Fact is information on a situation.

Faith is understanding of a situation.

Fact is yours or someone else's knowledge.

Faith is your belief.

Fact is external referencing created by or creating fear.

Faith is internal referencing created by or creating love.

Fact creates internal unrest and uncertainty.

Faith creates internal peace and confidence.

Fact requires external validation to confirm what you know is right.

Faith enables you 'to just know'.

Dimensions of Health

Creating a Balanced life - East vs. West

Modern western health experts sometimes use the Wellness Wheel to demonstrate the different dimensions we need to observe in order to obtain overall health and wellbeing.

This approach, however, can sometimes be taken too literally, and we often place too much emphasis on one segment at a time, rather than considering the whole wheel as a flowing cycle. For example, concentrating on only personal fitness and physical health without any consideration for spiritual knowledge or faith can create imbalance in the mind and over stimulate the body. By creating strength in one area but none in the other, the wheel cannot roll. Currently, there is a huge focus on mental health with little or no mention of how environmental, social and financial factors impact our ability to create balance. Without a sense of grounding, security and belonging, mental stability is almost impossible to attain.

The striving for a balanced life, however, is not a modern problem. Chinese culture dating back thousands of years refers to the ebb and flow of retaining balance in life as Yin and Yang, the pendulum that gently swings from passive to active, internal feelings to external actions, soft to hard etc. Balance is finding the gentle rhythm and flow in life. The ancient Aryan race dating back almost 4000 years brought the Sanskrit language to India which was the foundation of a yogic text called Sutra. They were a nomadic people who travelled by horse and ox-drawn carts and they introduced the following terms still used in yoga today:

Dukkha - meaning suffering.

Sukha – meaning happiness, ease or comfort.

The words refer to having a bad or good axle.

"It was a bumpy ride" (Dukkha)

"It was a smooth ride" (Sukha)

Suffering therefore translates to experiencing a bumpy ride. Life has ruts and it is inevitable that we experience bumps in the road, but it is the way life is perceived that is important, whether it is believed it to be bumpy or smooth.

Try using this analogy to help evaluate the effectiveness of your wellness wheel. Use the circle below and evaluate each section and consider how 'bumpy' your 'ride' is. If all areas are not equal, how can the wheel turn and you flow well to enable a smooth ride in life? Consider the sections which need support and development and look at ways to enrich them.

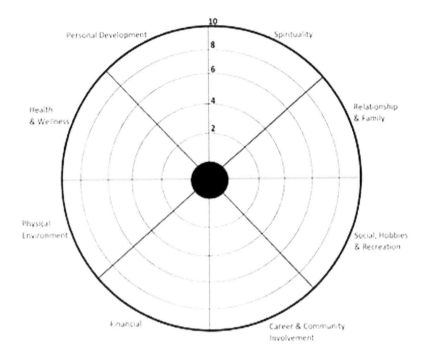

The Eight-Limbed Path of Patanjali is a form of lifestyle yoga which dates back several thousand years. It explains the many dimensions of health needed to create balance, peace and spiritual growth and forms the basis of learning within this book

Its philosophy starts with social grounding and understanding, which in turn brings you a sense of peace and belonging in your own life and within the world around you.

Next comes the creation of physical health through a comfortable body and correct breathing patterns. Physical comfort supports the creation of balance in the heart and when combined with a sense of belonging, brings joy and contentment into day to day life.

It is only with social grounding and physical comfort is in place that the mind can focus and expand, creating true spiritual clarity and good mental and emotional stability. All the above aspects are gently grown together, creating the tree of life. Like gentle building blocks, each area supporting and encouraging growth in other areas.

To know where you are heading in life

to be open to the expanse of opportunity and wonder available to you,

you must first understand and accept, without judgement,

where you have been and how you have come to this crossroad.

Only then can you move forward with instinct and insight.

Dear Reader

My initial journey was a time of self-reflection and setting out new expectations for myself and the people around me. At times this was a huge challenge. I had spent most of my adult life as a people pleaser, putting others before myself and taking the road of least resistance for an easier life. Does this sound familiar?

I felt I had too much to do and no time for myself. I was physically exhausted, unable to function consciously and proactively, emotionally or mentally. Life basically felt like a huge void, just about to swallow me up. I felt lost.

However, our body and soul have a way of sending us signals, and nature, in its ultimate wisdom, was there to ensure I stopped dead in my tracks and took stock of my life.

Within a six-month period, my marriage ended, I lost my job, had no money, and, to top it all off, I had a bad accident, which meant I spent three months in plaster. I moved out of my *ego house and rented a small colliery terraced house with very little furniture or belongings.

However, if you look positively at every life lesson or experience given to you, great things can happen. Out of these terrible six months came a wonderful new beginning. They say that when you lose everything, and are stripped bare, you see life with great clarity. I have found this to be true. During this time, I gained my roots, I set out my new standard in life and decided what I was going to accept in myself and in others. I set myself goals to achieve; some very small, some bigger. Every time I achieved a small goal, I became stronger and I acknowledged that completing tasks built my resilience. I got myself back to physical fitness and discovered, through understanding my body better and learning to breath correctly, that I was able to be focused and positive, to find solutions and open the pathway to mine and my daughter's future. For the first time in my life, I felt free. In fact, I felt more than that, I felt alive and full of hope and excitement at what could be.

So, please spend time creating your roots, learn to respect and admire your achievements. Once you have a solid foundation, you will be truly immovable!

*Ego is defined as one's image of oneself, or the conscious mind, which is based on one's perception through external referencing. It can also be defined as conceit or a sense of self-importance. In the world of yoga, ego (*ahamkara*) is defined as the individual's sense of who they are – their thoughts, desires and personality, as shaped by the primal mind, which is the survival of the fittest where the strong lives off the weak. It is sometimes referred to as the "false self," because it is colored only by one's view of the world.

<u>Notes</u>

Eight Limbs to Happiness

The Pathway of Patanjali

The more we exist in a virtual world, the less we *'live'* in the real one. This creates an ever-greater divide between us and the natural world we live in. In a virtual world we can create a whole new persona, with ten thousand 'friends' on social media and an amazing imaginary lifestyle. However, the more time that is spent with your head in a computer, tablet or phone, the less time you spend cultivating genuine friendships, and real life can pass you by unnoticed.

Humans are pack animals and as such we thrive on social interaction. We develop and expand our knowledge and ideas through face to face contact and social interaction. Solitary confinement, on the other hand, has been proven to be a very effective form of mental and emotional torture.

So, it will come as no surprise that living a modern, disconnected life can have a massive negative impact on our mental and emotional health. The result has been an explosion of issues such as loneliness, depression and anxiety, spreading through society at the same rate as the development of isolating technology.

Many lifestyle illnesses such as stress, eating disorders, body dysmorphia (to name just a few) can be eased by talking and connecting with others. Human contact creates a bond of trust, which results in an uplift in confidence and self-esteem. Conversely, living online does not provide the energetic connection that we need to gain a positive sense of belonging.

When your head is in the digital cloud you are no longer connected to nature, to life, or to your true self.

Developing roots in life is the first step to feeling secure within yourself and creating a calmer and more contented way of living. With any journey the first steps are always the most difficult, full of trepidation and fear of the unknown. It may feel overwhelming and impossible to know where to start, or you may feel frightened to let go of current lifestyle choices. So, start small, and repeat to yourself, "I can, I will, I do" (a mantra for confidence).

True happiness can only be gained from looking within. You will never find contentment and peace by searching outwardly, as object referencing is ego based and the ego always loses in the end. To find real peace, you must look to your heart.

Object-referrals are external influences which have become part of modern, media-based everyday life. They are situations, people, objects of 'need'. Living within an ego-based world which is object-referenced requires continuous approval from others and an expectation to be judged on your looks, car, house, job, self-image etc.

These behaviors are based on fear, fear of being judged, fear of failure or not being good enough, and limit your true life potential as you become focused on maintaining your image.

This creates anxiety, stress, anger and disharmony within the body as object referral is a temporary state and cannot be maintained long term. When the job goes, the house goes, the fancy car goes, the money goes, you are left with nothing. You are empty.

Self-referrals are internal influences; your heart, conscience and your mind all working together. You do not fear other people's opinions and thoughts as you have opened yourself up to your true potential with no limitations. You become fearless.

These behaviors are based on the principle of love, where you become immune to criticism and you feel inferior to no one while also being humble enough to know you are superior to no one.

The first step to happiness is to make everyone and everything in nature equal to you, you are no more, or less important than anyone or anything else on this blue planet.

Within Hatha yogic philosophy, you will find the eight-limbed pathway (or the eight considerations) which gives guidance to enable you to live a peaceful, open life. This will allow you to first see and then achieve your life lesson, your purpose for being.

Following the eight-limbed principles will support your development to self-referral, reduce the ego and enable you to experience true happiness in your life.

There are eight topics to consider...

Yama   Five observations towards others' happiness.

Niyama   Five observations towards oneself.

Asana   Posture and a strong, healthy body.

Pranayama   Control of the life force / breath.

Pratyahara Withdrawal from external influences.

Dharana   Development of focus and concentration.

Dhyana   Meditation and absorption.

Samadhi   The journey to pure love and contentment.

Finding your roots involves the first four topics and requires a reassessment of your current lifestyle and choices, along with the development of personal disciplines and a firm commitment to change for the good.

1 and 2

Yama and Niyama

Limbs one and two cover the development of 'quality of being' towards others and oneself. Essentially, they are how to become a good person. In ancient times students could spend many years on this section alone before their master would allow them to proceed onto yogic learning. Modern lifestyles rarely consider the importance of appreciation and respect of oneself and others, but yogic philosophy considers them the foundations of a peaceful life. To reduce turbulence in life, you must have grounding and strong principles to live by. Yama and Niyama are these principles.

In following chapters, Limbs three and four, Asana and Pranayama, pertain to the attainment of physical excellence. The creation of a healthy, strong, natural body allows the soul to develop, expand and travel well. When combined, these create the four elements of grounding, enabling you to set down roots and live a heathy life.

Limbs three and four are the most recognizable and what most people associate with yoga practice using physical postures and breathing techniques to improve their health, fitness and sense of calm. However, what is accomplished on the mat for an hour or two each week only scrapes the surface of what Asana and Pranayama really encompass.

As you read through this book, you will discover that each limb has specific requirements and goals to achieve. However, there is no single defined route, as each limb is intrinsically entwined with the others.

Imagine your journey like a cherry blossom tree, starting with small roots and branches, weak and needing support. As the roots grow and spread, bringing more nourishment to the trunk it becomes bigger and stronger and able to support the upward growth of the branches. Your journey develops like the tree, as the roots (your principles) become more embedded, your body and energy levels (the trunk) grow in strength and the branches and blossom (your spiritual freedom and personal peace) become more far-reaching and open. Over several years the tree becomes strong both in its root system and branches and enables the creation of the most amazing beauty (for the benefit of others) through its blossom, unwavering for the rest of its life.

Yama

Five Observations Towards Others' Happiness

The five commitments to others will support change in the way you see others and the world around you, enabling you to live peacefully in society and nature. It offers the focus to change from negative thought and deed to positive and supportive language and emotions, which, in turn, will allow the mind and heart to feel at ease. If you put love and kindness out into the world, you receive it back.

Non-violence – To cause violence to society causes pain to yourself. Become non-violent in thought and deed. Become more empathetic to others and consider their views. Do not criticise other people's actions, they are not yours.

Truthfulness – Be honest in all actions and intentions to others and do so with kindness and love. Take a moment to consider others' situations and try not to sit in judgement over their actions. If you do not judge, you are equal, and you will see the true picture.

Non-coveting – Do not miss what you do not or have never had. Envy creates negativity and increases the ego, which, in turn, damages the feeling of contentment within society and increases the personal feeling of failure.

Non-stealing – Do not overload yourself with others' thoughts or criticisms. Do not steal by taking up others' time selfishly or drain their energy with your own negativity.

Preservation and cultivation of life's vital energy – Don't get bogged down with small problems, instead, see the bigger picture and do not be drawn into negative actions which drain your energy. Instead, choose wisely the recipients of your loving energy and perpetuate postitivity.

Implementing your commitments concerning others' happiness.

On each page, identify a person who is significant within your life and that you feel you can support. This needs to be someone outside of work, where you get no personal or financial gain from seeing them thrive.

Name:

How do you know this person?

What principle(s) can you commit to your relationship with
this person?

How will this make their life better?

Name:

How do you know this person?

What principle(s) can you commit to your relationship with this person?

How will this make their life better?

Name:

How do you know this person?

What principle(s) can you commit to your relationship with this person?

How will this make their life better?

Niyama

Five Observations Towards Oneself.

(Personal commitments for inner development.)

Personal cleanliness – Both inside and out. Keep the physical body clean and fresh and have consideration for a tidy appearance. Ensure the body is nourished with healthy, 'real' food without chemicals and preservatives. A lighter, simpler diet supports the body and subsequently the mind to be cleansed and improve in health.

Happiness – Make a personal commitment to be happy. Accept circumstances as they are and give thanks for the things you DO have. There really is always someone more in need than you.

Forbearance – Sometimes the more challenging route has the best life lessons. What you can change for the good – change.

What you cannot change – accept.

Instead, redirect energy to enthusiastically engage life to achieve the goal of creating union between the physical body, the mental body and the spiritual body.

Self-study – Observe your body, mind and emotions and strive to become a better person. Consciously observe your intentions and reactions in every activity, accepting with grace current limitations, and create a nurturing environment for your personal development.

Love the divine – Acknowledge and revel in the understanding that there is a greater power which will guide you (if you listen) down your true path. Embrace your religious, cultural and personal beliefs and be true to yourself, always. Have faith in the world and yourself and it will become a better place.

Yama and Niyama, the ten simple principles to live by, are the cornerstone to a peaceful existence. Becoming a good person, with honest principles and confidence in your own ability, leads to a fairer approach to others. You become more grounded.

These principles will be woven through the contents of this book and, as you commit to a better you, it will become clear that in order to grow, you need *your* foundations, *your* principles to live by.

Take some time to look at your current approach to yourself and the people around you and set yourself your own Ten Commitments to a happier life.

The Ten Commitments for my life journey.

I make a promise to myself to be…

To others…

1

2

3

4

5

To myself…

1

2

3

4

5

Place these commitments in a prominent place in your home and look at them every day

Notes

3. Asana

Taking Back Personal Responsibility

Over several hundred years man has looked further and further outwards, neglecting inward knowledge. With the development of modern technology, we now know more about getting the best out of our mobile phones than we do about getting the best out of our bodies.

Ask someone where their kidneys are and what they do, and they may not to know. Ask someone to explain the sequence of the organs and their importance to your health within the digestive system, and you can often be met with a blank expression. However, we still act surprised when our bodies falter or fail.

We expect doctors to fix whatever state we present our neglected bodies in, then refuse to accept the prognosis when there is nothing to be done. Keeping a person physically alive is the priority of doctors, keeping the 'self' *well* is ours.

Step three in the path of life is to take back personal responsibility for your own health and wellbeing. You would not expect a stranger to maintain and be responsible for the upkeep of your most precious belongings like your home, car, or your bank balance. So why would you be happy to remove any personal responsibility or accountability for your body, or your life?

The most precious thing you will ever have is natural health and ease within your physical form, so learn about how to stay well, peacefully, within the balance of nature. Respect the amazing work that goes on inside you every day, without you even knowing, and you will never neglect yourself again.

The media is obsessed with what your outer shell looks like, creating the illusion that this is more important than what is taking place within. When, in reality, what goes on behind the scenes is truly amazing.

Yogis believe that the real you is not your physical body. They believe that the 'soul' or 'vital force', the immortal 'I' (being or true self) is not the mortal body it occupies. The body is simply like a suit of clothing that the soul puts on and then takes off once it has completed its work. This is the same within every living creature, they have a soul, requiring respect and care.

Visualize your body as a temple, worthy of development and care. Create the best 'structure' you can achieve, as an unhealthy body does not allow the mind (soul) to function properly, and the instrument (physical body) cannot be used effectively to complete your life journey or lesson.

More simply put, a healthy body leads to a happy, healthy mind, which leads to a content, fulfilled life with purpose of being.

The Divine Architect

Over millions of years mother nature has offered every living creature on this planet gifts to support it in its life quest. Perfecting the physical casing (body) of each soul to adapt to its environment and thrive. Science calls it evolution.

The human body is constantly on alert, so it can repair damage, heal wounds, grow new bones when broken, and remove as quickly as possible any harmful materials from the body. This then allows the soul to get on with its task of learning.

Humanity has been given a wonderful piece of equipment by Mother Nature. Our bodies support the development and expansion of our souls as they travel on their journey and can, when healthy, enable us to complete our life lesson.

When Mother Nature created the human body, there were ten considerations observed to ensure the Soul could flourish.

The Soul needs a highly organized physical instrument of thought and a central station to direct the work of the body. Nature provided the Soul with the brain. The possibilities of the brain are only faintly recognized at this moment in time as we only use a tiny amount of its capacity to control our physical functionality.

The Soul needs organs designed to receive and record the impressions of our lives on the external world. Nature provided the Soul with eyes to see and observe, ears to hear, the nose to smell, taste buds to explore foods and detect poisonous substances before entering the body, and nerves on our outer layer to feel.

The Soul needs the means to communicate between the brain and the other parts of the physical body. Nature provided the Soul with a circuit of communication wiring. The brain sends signals through the wiring to all parts of the body, sending orders to the cells and organs insisting on immediate obedience. The brain then receives messages back, warnings of dangers, calls for help, complaints etc.

The Soul needs the means to move around. Nature provided the Soul with limbs, muscles and tendons so the physical body can reach out, touch and turn external objects into items for its own use.

The Soul needs a framework to hold its shape and protect it from shock or impact, giving it firmness and strength. Nature provided the Soul with the bony frame called the skeleton.

The Soul needs the means to communicate with other embodied souls. Nature provided the Soul with the functions of speech and hearing.

The Soul needs a system of repair for the whole body, to build up and strengthen its structure. Nature provided the Soul with the life-carrying blood within the arteries and veins where it carries out its work. Creating and distributing new raw materials to create and maintain a healthy body and a vehicle to collect up diseased and damaged cells.

The Soul needs a system to absorb fresh vital energy into the body and the ability to remove waste. Nature provided the Soul with the lungs to absorb energy from the oxygen it draws in and removes the waste on the out breath, in the form of carbon-dioxide.

The Soul needs materials from nature to use as raw materials for building, maintaining and repairing the physical body. Nature provided the Soul with the means to eat natural foods which are full of raw materials. She provided the means to digest and extract the nutrients, converting them into elements for use within the body for cell generation. She also provided the ability to flush out harmful elements and waste matter.

The Soul needs the means to reproduce. Nature provided the Soul with the miracle of reproduction. The creation of new vessels for new souls.

Re-read this section a few times to fully absorb the truly amazing creation you are and the magnitude of what is going on behind the scenes. Then, ask yourself, am I giving my body the respect it really deserves and am I helping myself to maintain and improve my own health?

Hatha yoga provides a strong, healthy, natural

physical body which allows the soul to develop,

expand and travel well.

Notes

Jot down any areas where you feel you are currently NOT supporting your body in its pursuit of health.

Now jot down what small things you can start to do to change this.

The Physical Body is Not Real.

The body as you know it is not a set structure, rather, it is a process, constantly changing.

The body you have now is not the body you had last year, and you can influence the body that you will have next year by starting to make changes now.

Did you know…

The stomach recycles every five days

The skeleton recycles every three months (hence why you are in plaster for approximately 12 weeks if you break a bone)

DNA stores memories for millions of years of evolution. However, the raw material, making current memories, changes every six weeks. You are creating your own DNA footprint every day and so, you can change the health of your body by your daily decisions and actions

So the question you must ask yourself is do you reinvent the same pattern of ill health and problems over and over, each time increasing the amount of dis-ease in the body OR do you choose to change for the better, creating a healthy way to live and thrive in the world today?

Your physical bodily restraints are fiction – what you believe, you will become.

Building Health

Nature has given you four supplies of health-giving energy or in yogic terminology, Prana, which every living organism on this planet utilizes and thrives on. 'Prana' in ancient Sanskrit language means 'absolute energy'. It is also known as 'Chi' in eastern countries and as 'vitality' in the west. It is the body's electrical charge which maintains life. Without Prana you die. (Prana is described in greater detail in Limb 4 – The control of the breath or life force.)

Prana from the sun promotes growth and repair.

Prana from water promotes hydration and fluidity within the whole body.

Plant-based food is eaten by all living creatures. This prana perpetuates the cycle of energy on earth. Eat nature's produce, fresh and colorful and stay away from preserved and processed 'edible substances' as they hold no energy.

Breathe fresh air and breathe well. This will maximize the amount of Prana received from the air you breathe. Also remember that oxygen, when drawn into the lungs, incinerates ill health within the body, breathing it out as carbon dioxide. The cycle of conscious breathing improves health with both the in-breath and the out-breath.

To support the four health-giving elements, the physical body needs to be exercised with a balanced practice of energizing and relaxing movements. If you only partake in active or passive activity the body is not balanced.

Positive stress is good for the body if it is balanced with equal quantities of structured relaxation.

The higher the physical stress, the deeper the physical relaxation needs to be to bring about balance. On the same note the lower the mood, the higher the mental simulation needs to be to gain balance emotionally.

Notes

Take time out to evaluate your current weekly activities and note the following…

Hours of physical exertion (stress) each week you put onto the body. (working, gym, running etc.)

Hours of mental exertion (stress) each week (work, home, personal issues)

Hours of physical relaxation each week (structured activities to remove tension from the body – not vegetating in front of the TV)

Hours of mental relaxation each week (structured activities focusing on rebalancing the mind)

What is your current imbalance?

The Importance of Relaxation

Many people in today's society spend most of their waking hours absorbed in physical or mental exertion and do not invest in rebalancing the mind and body with structured relaxation.

Many people have forgotten how to relax, or, if they have not, it's a rare occurrence. When you are not relaxed, the mind is on alert, looking for possible danger, searching for external potential risks and hazards. This increased sense of distraction means concentration becomes almost impossible to achieve, as this would require suppressing the external-looking, natural turbulence in the mind. The primitive brain's most basic instinct is to protect therefore it is important to learn techniques to remove the turbulence.

Concentration spontaneously occurs in a naturally relaxed body and mind, so until relaxation is achieved, true concentration is not possible. Therefore, the first step on your journey of spiritual and mental development is to learn to relax!

Regular yoga practice supports the rebalancing of the physical body and the subtle body and supports the path to self-development through conscious awareness, widely known as Mindfulness.

Awareness is the conscious attention of thoughts or of objects, either internally or externally, without being one-pointed (having a goal or expectation). This is not meditation, it is paying attention to something or a train of thought, following it, observing it, and understanding the effects it has on you physically, emotionally and mentally. Awareness means not suppressing thoughts or emotions, even if they do not seem relevant to the current moment. Instead, allow them to gently rise and then disappear, observing them without emotional attachment or judgment.

Practicing awareness creates activity in your conscious self, opening the mind to true potential and allowing coordination to develop between the nervous system and the mind. If the mind is calm, the body can relax. If the body is physically relaxed, so is the mind.

There is one more dimension to this equation - the immune system.

A calm mind + a relaxed body = a strong immune system.

There is an infinite array of ways to gently relax the body and the mind. However, the question to ask yourself is, does it bring you joy? Whenever you embark on an activity without truly enjoying it, you only create more dis-ease in the body as you are not following your true path. If it makes you smile and fills you with enthusiasm then, no matter what the activity, it is right for you at this moment in your life. So, do it.

If you are happy in your activities, your body will physically relax and become more at ease. This will enable the body to get on with its real job of healing and improving, instead of crisis management. Proactively look for joy-giving activities, which also re-affirm your commitment to change and involve the four elements of energy-giving in everyday activities.

For example...

A daily walk incorporates air, sun and balancing exercise. Take a walk with another person, and you will also gain healthy, social interaction. A healthy lunch should incorporate nourishment and water.

Positive, healthy interaction is vital for balancing the whole body, both physically and mentally. So, spending time with your real friends and confidants is as important as eating well. You get energy from the people around you, and happy people give off happy energy.

Developing a good sleep routine supports the balancing of the nervous system and immune system as sleep is the body's natural healing time. So, switch off the electronics at least 30 minutes before you go to bed to support the body's change to a healthier lifestyle. While you are sleeping the internal body is working to restore health, flushing out toxins and cleaning the organs. Learn to love your sleep and look forward to waking up a bit healthier every day.

Maximizing Restful Sleep

According to the teachings of Purna Yoga (a form of Hatha yoga, which teaches love-centered practice) the following is observed:

Every hour you sleep before midnight is equivalent to one and a half hours of rest.

Every hour you sleep between midnight and 6am is equivalent to one hour of rest.

Every hour you sleep after 6am is equivalent to half an hour of rest.

Therefore, you should go to bed early and get up early to maximize the body's rest time.

24 Hours in the Life of Digestion

The food you eat each day creates most of the energy used to support the maintenance and repair of the physical body. This food also provides the energy needed to accomplish the daily requirements of life and work.

Good digestion depends on a well-balanced body and mind, and the best way to achieve this is through awareness and regulation of the energy (prana) within the body.

Imagine the digestive system as an oven with a temperature gauge which fires up when food is consumed and cools down when resting. The Prana combined with bile within the stomach produces heat needed to digest food and convert it into energy. When combined with mucus, the digestive system produces a cooling effect within the stomach. The mucus brings the temperature of the digestive system back down to a natural level at the end of the conversion process. Thus, the digestive system is balanced and the gastric fire is kept not too hot and not too cold. If the body has too much gastric fire it can cause problems such a gastric ulcer and diarrhoea, if the food is too cold it can cause conditions such as asthma.

For example, if you have a hot curry, your nose runs as it creates mucus to cool the gastric fire. Or, if you drink a very cold drink on a sunny day it can create a wheeze in the throat and make the lungs contract. This is because there is not enough gastric fire.

Food should be eaten when there is a balance between the gastric fire and the mucus in the body. Most forces within the body work on a daily cycle, naturally peaking at certain times during the day. Meals should be eaten in line with the natural ebb and flow of this rhythm to maintain balance within the body. However, many people living hectic lives do not understand the workings of their body. In fact, most people know more about their favorite celebrity than they do about their digestive system, eating at any time of the day and night and then being surprised when the body becomes uncomfortable and dis-eased.

According to the school of thought surrounding acupuncture, the following time periods indicate when the organs of the digestive system are at their most effective.

AM			PM
Lungs	3-5am	___	Bladder 3-5pm
Large intestine	5-7am	___	Kidneys 5-7pm
Stomach	7-9am	___	Heat components 7-9pm
Spleen	9-11am	___	Metabolic process 9-11pm
Heart	11am-1pm	___	Gall Bladder 11pm-1am
Small intestine	1-3pm	___	Liver 1-3am

The times listed above indicate when the organs are at their peak, full of energy and able to function at optimum capacity. Therefore, the opposite times in the day are when they are at their weakest, or lowest level of energy. You can see, therefore, there is an optimum time during the day to eat a meal. The stomach is most receptive to processing food between 7am and 9am and so eating late at night is going to cause problems.

"Eat breakfast like a king, lunch like a lord and supper like a pauper."

By eating your main meal of the day between 7 and 9am the food reaches the small intestines at its optimal time to be absorbed into the body, between 1pm and 3pm. A healthy, slow-releasing morning meal should always be your main meal of the day, as it fuels the body with energy for the whole day. After all, you would not expect to be able to drive your car on a long journey without first filling up the tank.

The reverse is true for eating late at night and then going to bed soon after. During the night, the bodily functions are cleaning, flushing and repairing. Digestion functions are very low and so the body stores rather than uses food consumed. This way of life is detrimental to your long-term health and one of the biggest factors in the many digestive health problems seen today. These include stomach ulcers, irritable bowel syndrome, acid reflux, constipation or diarrhea and heart burn, to name just a few.

There are many other lifestyle ailments which can be routed back to the incorrect timing of eating and which, therefore, can be helped by eating your main source of nourishment before midday.

From 7am and 3pm the body is ready to receive the raw materials needed to create health in the body. When consumed at this time the correct balance of digestive juices is produced, the heart's rate begins to increase and breathing strengthens to ignite the absorption process. Between 3pm and 7pm the absorbed nutrition is being utilized in the body and the digestive system begins to slow and empty, flushing out the waste and tidying up after a busy day. While it is still possible to eat at this time digestion is not as effective, so lighter foods are recommended. Then, from 7pm to 3am, the body is cleaning and sterilizing the system, removing toxins and poisons from the body ready to be expelled. Between 3am to 5am the lungs are working at their maximum to burn off, or carbonate the dead, damaged or diseased cells. Finally, from 5am to 7am, the large intestines condense the unusable substances ready to be eliminated from the body on awakening.

There are many people who graze continuously during the day, snacking and drinking without consideration for the timetabling of food. Continuously eating will not allow the body to become hungry and so makes the digestive system toxic and you will feel dis-eased. When the stomach is constantly in use, the fire of digestion is unable to be ignited and the system unable to be cleaned. It is the pang of hunger which sets off the chain reaction within the digestive system, igniting the heat to cleanse the system and burn off toxins and impurities before receiving the next supply of food to digest.

Visualize what your pans would be like if you never stopped to clean them between meals and used it repeatedly. They would be full of bacteria and germs. The same applies to your stomach and intestines

It is vital to acknowledge that every organ within the digestive system has a purpose and a sequence in which it works. Imagine your body like a factory production line, it would be the most efficient example of 'time and motion' you are likely to witness. Respect the process, understand that to live a healthy life with vitality and peace, you must work *with* the body, supporting the amazing process of digestion that has been developed over millions of years. Eat real foods at the right time so your body can repair you and keep you well.

Food for thought

More people die in the world today through overeating than from hunger.

Obesity-related cancers are the fastest growing concern to health today.

Eat to support the Natural Rhythm of your body.

Make gentle changes to when and what you eat.

This will improve your health.

Timetabling your Meals

In the morning – Provide your body with the raw materials it needs to create new healthy cells and to carry out maintenance and repair work. Provide your body with energy needed to carry out normal daily functions such as breathing, walking, thinking and talking.

Invest in breakfast! Eat well to fuel the body and mind

Lunchtime – Your body has dissolved the raw materials and absorbed them into your blood stream to do the required work. It has also identified any toxins and poisons and begun to remove them and stored them in the appropriate 'safe place'. A smaller top up of raw materials (food) should be consumed at this point to keep the fire going.

Evening – Eat as light and small a meal as possible, as the 'Nightshift' work is being carried out. Your digestive fire is dampened down to allow the cleaning out of the whole digestive system, flushing through, incinerating harmful chemical and cell waste, preparing to eliminate the unusable raw materials the next morning.

The next morning – Your digestive fire ignites as you have breakfast (the breaking of your fast) and the waste is removed from the body; the digestive system is ready to start again.

Being aware of the process of digestion you can start to appreciate the negative impact that consuming a heavy meal, with alcohol, has on your body, especially late at night.

Choosing the correct raw materials to consume is very important and nature has created the cures and preventatives for most ailments within the body. Eating a lighter diet with a wide range of plant-based ingredients, provides the best materials possible to ensure your new body (created by the cells made with the food you eat) will be healthier and more vibrant.

White foods such as onions, garlic & leeks. provide essential pre-biotics into the gut, which then make natural pro-biotics to support the immune system.

Green foods such as broccoli, sprouts, cucumbers, green beans, spinach etc. provide the body with detoxification and purification.

Red foods such as cranberries, cherries, bell peppers, raspberries, strawberries, tomatoes etc. improve heart and blood health.

Yellow foods such as banana, lemons, limes, squashes, avocado etc. fortify the skin's elasticity.

Orange foods such as cantaloupe, carrots, mangoes, pumpkins, sweet potatoes, oranges (whole) etc. support the formation of anti-bodies to fight off disease.

Purple foods such as blackberries, blueberries, cabbage, currants, eggplant, plums etc. increase longevity.

In addition:

Zinc supports the healing of wounds.

Can be found in foods such as beans, nuts, whole grains & milk.

Vitamin E provides anti-oxidants and reduces free radicals (toxins).

Can be found in foods such as almonds, hazelnuts & spinach.

Vitamin A regulates the immune system.

Can be found in foods such as sweet potato, kale, spinach & bell peppers.

N.B. This list is in no way exhaustive of all the health implications of eating a natural diet. They are simply examples of the variety of health-giving nutrients found in nature's foods. There are many other vitamins, minerals and health-related properties within all plant-based foods that are not mentioned here.

Spend time exploring the wonders of natural foods and how they will improve your health long-term.

Spend time looking at the benefits of eating 9-10 natural foods per day and their correct portion sizes.

Eat more whole-grain foods and begin to consider meats as a treat rather than part of every meal, as they are hard to digest and eliminate from the body.

Make a list of your favorite plant-based foods and see what properties they have.

When creating your meals, try to incorporate as many colors as you can to ensure you are giving your body the tools it needs to improve your health.

The Benefits of Yoga Practice

The term yoga translates to the word 'union'.

Yoga practice allows you to realize your connection with the greater self, to recognise and tune into your existing or true nature. In other words, yoga can be seen in and defined as part of everyday normal life. When people feel separation from, or do not understand the possibility of a higher self (true potential in life), they are not at one or comfortable with themselves. When they have a low level of consciousness their potential becomes clouded and they are prevented from accessing the higher self and personal identity.

Yoga enables you to understand that, with practice and discipline, a higher level of awareness can be achieved through strengthening the physical body and improving energy levels. This in turn creates a sense of calm to enable a true reflection of your heart and mind's potential to steadily evolve.

There are many paths in yoga, in fact Hindu books list over 100 styles that have been adapted over many years to suit different temperaments and goals. You could say that every person practicing yoga has a different style as each person is unique in their form and intention but, like rivers, they all run the same way, joining together in the great expansive ocean. Just like the river loses its individual identity when it reaches the vast ocean, the same can be said about the different paths of yoga. At first, they are very specific about characteristics and some seem to contradict each other, but along the line, one by one their differences disappear. All paths of yoga have the same goals: physical health, mental peace and higher awareness.Traditionally there are five main pathways of yoga, they are followed depending on the student's learning needs or spiritual calling. Each path, in turn, has many limbs of learning extending from it.

The five main Paths of Yoga

Hatha Yoga – The Path of Balance

Karma Yoga – The Path of Activity

Bhakti Yoga – The Path of Devotion

Jnana Yoga – The Path of Enquiry

Raja Yoga – The Path of Introspection

Each path of yoga contains qualities of the other four, just as human nature also has many facets. All of us have tendencies to be introspective and enquire about the nature of our life, just as we have emotions and perform actions (make choices). Lastly, everyone has a mind and body, which can often fight against each other. It is all these aspects that make up a person's personality and traits. For example, some people are more emotional or more devotional than others.

Choosing the style of yoga for your journey, to suit your true nature, can initially be very daunting - what if you choose the wrong one?

So, don't. Instead, start in the ocean and learn the fulness of yoga first. Then be guided by your true nature as you reach the river that feels the most instinctive. At this point you will be ready to open to your higher self.

Hatha Yoga – The Path of Balance

The path of balance is a great place to start. 'Ha' means Sun and 'tha' means Moon. Therefore, the practice of Hatha yoga focuses on the harmony between the sun and the moon aspects of your being, bringing balance to every area of your life.

The right side of the body and airwave (the right nostril) connects to the Sun aspects, and the left side of the body and airwave (the left nostril) connects to the Moon aspects. The Sun controls the vital and physical functions of the body and the Moon controls the mental functions.

In yogic philosophy, health is defined as a combination of resistance to infection;

absence of dis-ease;

mental and physical endurance;

flexibility of mind and body;

mental peace;

perfect coordination and condition of all organs, muscles and nerves in the body and their control by the brain and spinal nerve centers, together with a perfectly functioning pranic* body. Hatha yoga aims to bring about this state of health.

Pranic body- is the energetic self. The ability to generate, store and use energy effectively and efficiently within the body. It is the sense of being alive and how it is projected out into the world and the use of energy to create joy and peace.

Yin vs. Yang

Most modern forms of exercise focus on YANG aspects; building strength and being energetic. YIN is the opposite side and focuses on deep muscle, breath, bones and spirituality. These Yin aspects are sometimes referred to as the subtle body.

DAO (the WAY) is the tranquility found at the centre of all events, it is balance in action, and the path leading to the centre. The centre is always there, even if you are not always there to enjoy it. Balance in life is being aware of your centre point and when you leave the centre, you take on aspects of YIN or YANG. The pendulum swings. The more out of balance you are the higher it swings from one side to the other.

YIN	YANG
Dark	Light
Cold	Hot
Passive	Active
Inside	Outside
Solid	Hollow
Slow	Rapid
Dim	Bright
Downward	Upward
Substance	Fiction
Water	Fire
Matter	Energy
Mysterious	Obvious
Female	Male
Moon	Sun
Night	Day
Earth	Heaven
Even	Odd
Plastic	Elastic

YIN ←--------------------------CENTRE------------------------→YANG

Passive   Calm, focused, attentive.   Active

Balanced

Modern-day lifestyles can create large swings within the pendulum.

YIN aspects of life take on internal references, such as the religious/spiritual belief you feel and your subtle body cultivating your personal YAMAs and NIYAMAs (observations to others and to yourself).

YANG aspects of life are driven by external references, or ego, which set out what western culture has required us to focus and thrive on, in a capitalist society.

YIN	YANG
Spiritual	Western Culture
The Bigger Picture	Focused
Losing/Letting Go	Winning
Fasting/Restraint	Consuming/Binge
Giving	Earning
Non-Attachment	Possessions
Observation	Decisiveness
Duty	Choice
Passive (Calm)	Active (Stress)

A YANG lifestyle is physically demanding on the body with very little time, if any, to rebalance the mind and heart.

For example, the Sunday morning energy vs. the rest of the week. Having a hectic Monday to Friday and a couch potato weekend can lead to either a Breakdown or a Breakthrough. You either crash and burn or you make a change, introduce structured YIN activities to rebalance.

A sedentary life with passive, negative thoughts brings mental depression, a lack of enthusiasm and low energy levels. To rebalance, introduce more YANG to activate and stimulate both your body and your mind.

To maintain long term health, your natural energy needs to be constantly moving gently, like a pendulum, swaying to and fro between stimulus and relaxation, self and others etc. So, during your daily activities, introduce a mixture of YIN and YANG aspects so you achieve a natural ebb and flow to your day. If the pendulum swings too far either way, you will lose this balance.

Hatha yoga is very popular as a means of achieving balance, as people tend to see tangible improvements quite quickly with regular practice. You will see improvements in personal fitness as well as feeling emotionally and mentally calmer than normal. However, it is important to understand that these benefits are a means to an end and not the actual end. This is only the beginning of your journey, and Asana practice (postures and movement) is there to support the development of your foundations of Yama and Niyama (personal observations to yourself and to others). The aim of Hatha yoga practice is to build a firm, strong, healthy body or temple, because without it you cannot achieve peace, happiness and contentment on your path.

Imagine your body as an instrument, which needs to be kept in its best condition as without it your spiritual development cannot gain strength. If a musician wants to play beautiful music, it is essential for the instrument to be in perfect working order. A virtuoso would not dream of trying to play a masterpiece on a broken, battered violin. It is the same with your path to higher awareness: the essential prerequisite is a well-tuned body and mind.

Karma Yoga – The Path of Action

Karma yoga is the system of attaining awareness through action. It is the performance of your daily work with constant awareness and, at the same time, without any expectation of reward. The selfless act. Volunteering is such an uplifting Karma because you are giving your time and energy selflessly without expectation of reward (money), and so the universe rewards you with a positive experience.

Obtaining presence of mind or being 'mindful' enables effective and more powerful actions in everyday life, as by absorbing yourself in the work at hand you reduce the effects of the *ego* and increase 'atma'- the sense of freedom from insecurities and the ability to show concern for others.

The path of Action states that every moment of every day you are making choices; a choice to get up or stay in bed, a choice to say yes or no to a new experience, a choice to be kind or to be selfish to others. Everything you accept, good or bad, everything you achieve or fail at is a choice you have made consciously or subconsciously and, most importantly, every time you create a 'self-limiting belief' you, and only you, are preventing yourself from achieving happiness in life.

What you give out in thought, word or deed, will return to you in even measures, as the universe needs to balance the books to keep energy flowing. So, keep your thoughts, words and deeds positive to yourself and others and you will receive positivity back. This is the natural circle of energy.

By doing this you will create less emotional and mental upset, making the mind calmer, clearer and more receptive to the practices of yoga and the possibilities now unfolding for you.

Mahatma Gandhi famously quoted the following;

'Keep your thoughts positive

because your thoughts

become **YOUR WORDS.**

Keep your words positive

because your words

become **YOUR BEHAVIOUR.**

Keep your behavior positive

because your behavior

becomes **YOUR HABITS.**

Keep your habits positive

because your habits

become **YOUR VALUES.**

Keep your values positive

because your values

become **YOUR DESTINY.'**

Bhakti Yoga – The Path of Devotion

Bhakti Yoga channels the emotions into devotion to others, directed towards a Guru, deity or object. In modern times it can be as simple as your love of knitting or crafts, cooking or choir. In this way your emotions are given an outlet instead of being suppressed, dissipating them in different directions. Bhakti absorbs itself into the focus of devotion therefore losing the ego. Mental or emotional problems disappear and the path to peace and a higher awareness of oneself opens. We will look at Bhakti in more depth later as part of development of concentration.

Jnana Yoga – The Path of Enquiry

Jnana Yoga is the enquiry into the essence of existence and your true nature. Effort, concentration and total absorption into your inquiry is needed for this path and so many find it is a pathway that they take much further on in their journey.

Jnana brings illumination into your life, intuitive understanding about things you may not feel able to talk about. Many of the greatest yogis have refused to talk about their personal illuminations as they feel it cannot be put into words. So, the route of cleansing the mind and developing concentration should be followed before opening to this path.

Raja Yoga – The Path of Introspection

Raja Yoga explores the different realms of the mind, conscious, subconscious, unconscious and beyond, to become more aware of the different aspect of your life. Raja Yoga helps you to understand why you may have made certain choices, to recognise your personal traits, strengths and weaknesses, and to develop good, strong morals.

Raja yoga develops consciousness, allowing you to move from just external consciousness to internal consciousness, directing your awareness inward and enabling you to explore yourself. If you only ever look at the surface of the ocean you miss out on the wonders held beneath. However, if you dive into the depths towards the seabed you will be able to see the deeper aspects of the mind. You can develop this path of yoga through Raja's many other limbs including:

Patanjali Yoga – The Eight-limbed Pathway (the basis of this book)

Kundalini Yoga – The Pathway of Prana (energy)

Mantra Yoga – The Pathway of Sound

Kriya Yoga – The Pathway of Awareness

By using a combination of these five pathways your health will gradually improve as you rebuild and reconnect with the body. You will gain understanding and respect for yourself, no matter what your current state of health at this moment in time. Give yourself unconditional love, do not judge or criticize the limitations which have been forced upon it by years of neglect. Instead, make a commitment to support the changes needed, give yourself the tools you need to repair and gain strength. Make your body your temple, for it is what holds your soul. It will, if you take care of it, allow your heart to be happy and your mind free to become great.

Respect yourself,

Love yourself unconditionally,

Give yourself permission to thrive,

And explore why you are here.

Notes

4. Pranayama

The Control of the Breath and Life Force

Out of the four required elements for life, air is the most immediate necessity for the physical, mental and emotional body to function and survive.

In certain parts of the world, life exists for months at a time without sunlight, and we know that man can survive for several weeks without food and several days without water. However, without air, man can live for only moments.

So, why is it that we neglect this function and allow it to become ineffective and faulted?

The correct breathing habits are essential for the continuation of vitality within the body and freedom against disease. Focused and intelligent control of the breath will support a longer, healthier life with continued vitality, while unintelligent and careless breathing creates a downward spiral of decreased health, reduced vitality, more disease and a shorter time to live your life.

The following is widely accepted within western society to be the way to enjoy a healthy life:

- Obtain nourishment from the food you eat – eat healthily.
- Water is good for you, especially spring water.
- The sun gives you a sense of uplifted mood and happiness.
- Exercise supports the development of good bone density and muscle strength and you should exercise for at least 30 minutes a day with moderate to high-level activities.
- Take deep breaths to calm the nerves.

Eastern cultures understand that there is a second reason for observing these steps for health. They recognise that within the food you eat, the water you drink, the sun you absorb, the exercise you do and each long slow breath you take, nature offers up a supply of energy to recharge your battery, increase your life force and maintain, as well as improve, your current state of health.

PRANA means absolute energy in ancient Sanskrit and can be found in every life form. It is the energy in all things and the higher the energy levels you have, the more energetic you will feel.

Nature gives a never-ending supply of energy through the air you breathe and through the balance of nature. Consider this, Mother Nature created balance in all things by first creating the plants and trees who live by "breathing" in carbon-dioxide and "breathing" out oxygen. Humans and animals evolved later as the natural recyclers of the trees' waste product, using oxygen as their source of energy and breathing out carbon-dioxide as a waste product, completing the cycle. Nature gives energy, life, vitality to sustain the cycle and gives us amazing tools to use. We just need to know where to look to find them.

The human body can extract Prana to improve health from many areas:

- Prana is found in large quantities in natural foods eaten to physically nourish the body.
- Prana can be drawn from the water used to cleanse and hydrate the body.
- Prana can be felt in the gentle heat and the mentally uplifting effects of the sun.
- Prana can be distributed around the body during physical exercise to bring balance to the mind and body.
- Prana is drawn into the body in large quantities through the air you breathe and recharges the battery of life, storing surplus for times of deficiency.

Prana is interwoven into every part of life and you can become healthier in every way by learning to extract and use it correctly. By doing so, you will maintain vitality to an old age and live well.

The most powerful source of Prana is through the breath. The air that is drawn into the body through intelligent breathing techniques should be thought of as a separate entity to oxygen. Energy or Prana is found in fresh air, and it can easily be explained by a simple example.

Picture a time when you have had to stay in your house for several days without venturing outside. During this period, you can breathe easily and function normally but after a while your mood starts to lower and your energy levels go down. This is because the air is now stale, and you have used up all the natural energy within the oxygen. By simply going outside for a short walk you feel uplifted because you are now breathing in fresh

Prana, recharging your battery and lifting your mood. You feel energized.

The **oxygen** is drawn into the body and used within the circulatory system, carried by blood to physically heal the body. However, **Prana** is a subtler entity as it is used by the nervous system to develop strength and vitality within the mind and emotions.

Oxygen does the physical, the ordinary;

Prana does the subtle, the extra-ordinary.

Oxygen	=	Physical body.
Prana	=	Spiritual and mental body.
Oxygen	=	Heals and maintains the physical body.
Prana	=	Heals and develops the mind.
Oxygen	=	Takes care of daily functions.
Prana	=	Builds 'life reserves' for future security.

Therefore, neglecting the four sources of energy not only affects physical health, it has a devastating effect on mental and emotional health. It causes the mind and heart to become unbalanced, starved of energy and unable to maintain clarity on a mental and emotional level.

Modern lifestyles have a detrimental effect on the absorption of Prana into the nervous system and the past 30-40 years, with the increase in processed food and technology, have seen a dramatic negative effect on mental and emotional health across all ages.

Food

Processed food containing chemicals, stabilizers, colorings and preservatives, to name just a few, are not a natural source of nourishment and cannot sustain the body in health and vitality. There is no Prana in these edible substances.

Water

The body requires water, nature requires it. Fizzy drinks, alcohol and caffeine-infused drinks do not hold Prana. Water does.

Sun

A lack of sunlight reduces the body's ability to absorb nutrients and Prana. The constant and almost obsessive use of sunblock prevents the body from absorbing the healthy rays, so use it wisely and seek advise on how and when to apply it. The early morning sun is the best for you. It is not about the heat, it's the light that matters.

Air

Staying indoors more and more means the body is breathing in stale air that has little or no Prana. The body can carry out physical functions, but subtle functions become lacking.

Exercise (5th element for distribution)

When you are lacking in Prana, excessive exercise can become a drawdown of what little energy you have stored. It can cause serious damage to the subtle body as well as the physical one, as the muscles become fatigued more quickly and eventually become damaged. The mind and emotions are drained of what little energy they have left, resulting in illnesses such as chronic fatigue syndrome and fibromyalgia, both examples of the effects of pushing the body too far when severely low in Prana.

When the body's battery becomes drained, the mind goes into crisis mode and the nervous system sends a distress signal around the body warning of imminent failure, bringing with it a feeling of anxiety and panic.

If it is unable to absorb energy organically through nature's elements, the body needs to find energy another way to stop the battery of life going flat and the body dying. Desperate times call for desperate measures and the body and mind work together to steal energy from other people, they become energy thieves.

Energy Thieves

It is no coincidence that the decline in traditional lifestyle choices and reduction of connection with nature has seen an increase in a state of aggression within society, both physically, and mentally. Greed, negativity towards others and general unrest has become the norm. Much of western society is 'starving'. This starvation is not through the lack of food however, it is through the lack of energy or PRANA.

As more and more people eat a processed diet and less natural plant-based foods, spend more time indoors alone on computers and less time outside physically connecting with nature and other people, drinking less water and more alcohol and caffeine-enhanced drinks and not thinking about others positively, they are no longer able to naturally recharge their life battery.

Instead, people are now trying to refill their batteries by stealing energy from those around them.

For example, two people in a healthy, balanced relationship feel equally relaxed and happy with a positive ability to cope with life. They achieve this by mutual respect and love, or in other words, they have a constant flow of positive energy between each other, both giving willingly to the other. This natural flow keeps the energy high and the person healthy by constantly replenishing and generating fresh energy.

Now consider, two people living in a destructive relationship. One dominant the other submissive, or both fighting for dominance. The dominant person is stealing energy from the submissive to make them feel better, full of life. The submissive party feels deflated and low as they have been stolen from. It becomes a cycle of stealing.

You will, like everyone, know someone who, after spending time with them, makes you feel exhausted. They are stealing your hard-won energy from right under your nose.

Would you allow this person to empty your bank account?

Would you notice?

The answer would be Yes.

Your life, health and personal happiness is more important than money, so learn to identify energy thieves and stop energy theft from happening to you.

Identifying your energy drains is important to be able to secure your long-term health. Energy is directly related to the stability of the mind and the emotions, which is vital for your ongoing survival and ability to strengthen resolve and move forward in a positive manner with fortitude of mind.

First, meet the *Intimidator.* This person gains your attention (steals your energy) by threatening you physically or mentally and insisting on your obedience by submitting to their will.

By giving them your time and attention (energy) you are surrendering to them. Long-term effects are a continuous drain of energy from you and an endless supply for the aggressor. The intimidator is known in western society as a bully and under extreme cases a dictator. The energy thief can have many sources of energy and the more they have the fuller they become, to the point where they feel invincible. The person being stolen from becomes physically weak, emotionally and mentally drained and unable to make decisions on their own. They can become full of dis-ease and can become seriously ill, even die.

Next, meet the *Interrogator.* This person is subtler but maintains an underlying sense of aggression. They keep your attention by undermining your decision-making and questioning your ideas, damaging their target's confidence and ability to make independent decisions.

The constant questioning and undermining of reason confuse the mind. The interrogator unbalances and unsettles their elected energy source and so gains a continuous flow of attention (energy) by ensuring the person is in constant need of their reassurance and approval for every action in their lives. As a person being stolen from, you lose confidence, self-esteem and become unable to function without outside approval.

The third energy thief is the *Aloof.* They steal your attention by keeping you second-guessing. They are vague and non-committal, evasive and play the 'silent critic' with sideway glances and tuts.

They are neglectful in emotional attention and so the source of the stolen energy becomes desperate for love and affection and will try tirelessly to gain approval and any form of acknowledgment that they are good and worthy. The aloof steals energy by unnerving or tricking you into the willing offering of your energy.

The fourth is *Poor Me,* or the guilt-tripper. They gain your attention by telling you all the terrible things that are happening to them. They tell you no one cares, life is so hard for them, you are guilt-tripped into feeling sorry for them and so allowing them to steal from you. They pour the guilt onto other people, nothing is their fault, they become the victim. They are the sympathy stealer.

Identifying the drains in your life is the first step to health, physically, emotionally and mentally. Once you have stemmed the flow of Prana (energy) from your body through theft you are able to start building your reserves.

It's one thing to become aware of the energy thieves around you but another to gently remove them from your circle of influence. Remember, a lot of the time these people will be long-term drains, they could even be a family member, so you need to take small steps: don't see them so often or make the decision not to get into negative conversations with them.

However, remember that this is a two-way street and you also need to look at your own behaviors.

Notes

Stealing energy as a way of life is quite addictive and can be difficult to change. The thieves are lazy and unwilling to create their own energy. They will find it challenging to start doing the work for themselves and will fight to keep their easy flow, through any means possible. It will also require them to let go of control over other people, letting go of the ego. They will no longer have as much vitality, power or strength and so will feel smaller. The same is applied to a thief who burgle peoples' homes so they have no need to work for a living. Holding down a steady job will cause lots of challenges, as they will be expected to live within the laws of society and become respectful of others.

But, most surprisingly, it can be just as much of a challenge to the person being drained. Stop to think for a minute. They have been living with their emotions, mind and body on high alert, battery almost on empty, for usually a long period of time. When the body is in crisis mode, all the senses are heightened, and the mind and emotions are crying out to be heard. The situation can quite often be exacerbated by using artificial stimulants to prevent total exhaustion or tranquilizers to help bring them down.

When the crisis is over the adrenaline reduces and the body calms, which can be very frightening because you become quiet, you are empty and have time to think. This can be terrifying. The body realises how exhausted it is, and this realisation can result in the last of the energy-draining situations.

The *Victim scenario* is when a person, who is so used to living on critically low levels of energy and therefore high alert, creates a situation to self-deplete when they feel their emotions or situation are quietening down. The reality of their life can become too difficult to cope with as they start to have time to feel and think. So, they self-drain. They create a new drama to keep other people's attention on them and their own energy level at critical. The mind and emotions return to high alert and away from the truth that their life is empty.

Knowing yourself better and understanding what you are doing means you can make informed decisions on your future. Instead of stealing Prana, look for ways to cultivate your own, in a calm and healthy way. While you continue to steal and be stolen from, your body remains in a state of panic and stress hormones race around the body making it very difficult to be proactive in the discovery of peace. Instead, you perpetuate a cycle of reactionary choices, more questions with no answers, magnifying the sense of mental and emotional instability, and life will start to fall apart.

To break the cycle, begin to change habits and look for ways to recharge naturally. As you start to feel more energy you will also start to feel more stable, less frightened and more confident in your own decision-making. This is a natural, steady process. By slowly reducing the amount of stolen energy you consume, and not allowing energy to be taken from you, along with creating your own, you will start to see a marked improvement within a relatively short period of time.

Top tips to create your own energy supply naturally:

Seek out simple foods, eat plant-based foods, as fresh as possible, grown naturally. If you eat meat, only eat meat from animals which have eaten naturally themselves and have not lived and died under stressful conditions. Eat organically. Steadily reduce the amount of sugars and chemicals within the body to bring yourself back to balance safely.

Drink water. Plain water flushes the body of toxins, however, to hydrate the body, add something to the water, such as a slice of lemon or piece of fruit, a natural tea. Simple.

Get outside. Go for walks, enjoy the countryside, parks, anywhere. Get some sunlight, just ordinary daylight as it doesn't have to be hot. Early morning light holds the best Prana.

Rest the body, allow your amazing body time to repair itself, create new cells and make you healthier. Help yourself to be healthier.

Learn to breathe well. Come away from stressful chest breathing and develop a conscious habit of using the whole lung through yogic techniques.

<u>Energy Stealers – Stemming the flow</u>

Make a list of your energy stealers and their type.

What can you personally do to gently prevent the loss of your energy?

Now think about the following....

Do **you** steal to survive on a daily basis?

How do you steal energy from the people around you?

Who do you currently steal from?

In times of crisis do you resort to stealing energy? If yes, what type of thief are you?

How can you stop the cycle of energy stealing in your life? What steps can you start to take to generate your own energy?

The Conscious Breath

Conscious breathing supports your development into building your personal supply of Prana, balancing your nervous system and mind. Conscious breathing allows you to make proactive choices or 'good karma', reducing the need for self-preservation or selfishness by reducing the influence of the primal brain (instinct) by re-energising the neocortex (the brain of reason).

If you have never consciously breathed before it can feel very difficult at first. The body breathes continuously every day of your life without you thinking about it, but over time, when left in the subconscious, you develop bad habits. So, when you begin to take note of your breathing process, you immediately start to question whether you are doing it correctly and the process can initially feel strained and difficult.

Instead of trying to change the process, observe at first, notice what is moving within the body and what is passive as your breath flows in and out.

Checking in on your breathing

Observe your breath during different times of the day and observe which part of the torso you are breathing from.

How do you feel...

First thing in the morning while calm and relaxed in bed?

At lunchtime at work, while you are eating?

At home, after a busy day?

After a confrontation when you have become stressed?

During a loving conversation when relaxed?

Last thing at night, just before you go to sleep?

Modern lifestyles will normally find you breathing high in the chest or mid chest, this indicates stress and that the body is needing higher levels of oxygen to function. This will normally happen during busy periods of the day.

Start to take more notice of the periods when you are calm, especially in the morning before you get out of bed and then in the evening, when you are about to sleep. You will become aware that the breath is coming from the abdomen. This is the natural way to breathe, and the body will revert to abdominal breathing when you are resting. However, due to a busy lifestyle, breathing habits have changed to cope with stress and the body automatically goes to high or mid breathing. Bringing abdominal breathing into everyday activity, and not just while you are resting, supports the change from reactionary to proactive behavior and will give the mind space to explore and be aware of what is going on around it.

Developing conscious breathing helps you take control of your own energy supply and, once mastered, you will never need to steal again as you will have an abundance of Prana, which will radiate from you.

You will find that you are happier to share your time, love and Prana with others, which in turn will create more vitality in your life as you receive back energy which is freely given. This creates a positive mutual exchange of Prana. You are no longer a drain, instead you are a radiator. You are someone people want to be around. You support and uplift others' energy levels by giving freely and unconditionally. This creates an upward spiral of energy for yourself and the people in your life and a sense of calm, happiness and peace in each day.

Your Energy

Who are your energy radiators?

How do you feel around them?

What activities do you do together to create a positive cycle of
energy with the people in your life?

Conscious Breathing Techniques

The following breathing techniques should be built up gradually. Start by learning to observe and direct the breath with abdominal movement, then build up the absorption of Prana through cyclic breath and finally, introduce positive affirmations to support your ongoing development.

Abdominal Breath

Abdominal Breathing is the basic technique used to relieve stress within the body. By using your stomach to breathe, you reduce tension within the chest, neck and shoulders, so aiding a sense of calm.

Once you have mastered the basic technique you will be able to look at further ways to enhance your mindfulness experience.

Steps:

Find a seated position, where the spine can gently support the body without tension and arms are comfortably resting on the thighs. If sitting on a chair the thighs and shins should be at 90 degrees to each other with the feet flat on the floor. Take off your shoes.

Relax the shoulders and roll them back then down. Clench the buttocks then let go.

Elongate the back of the neck and lift the crown of the head (top) slightly to the ceiling.

Close the eyes. Relax the jaw and let the tongue rest at the bottom of the mouth.

Observe the natural movement of the torso while breathing.

Place your right hand softly onto the upper chest.

Place your left hand over the belly button.

Keep arms relaxed and elbows low.

Observe which hand is moving.

Over the next few breaths consciously relax the chest, feel the movement becoming softer and the right hand becoming still.

Imagine the diaphragm as a hill, as you start to take the inbreath, visualize pushing down on the hill to make it flat. You will start to gently expand the belly as you breathe in and when you then relax, the belly will flatten, and the hill will rise back up on the outbreath. Feel the left hand starting to move gently.

Continue breathing through the belly for up to 5 minutes (or until you feel you need to return to a natural breath) with hands in place.

Release hands down to your thighs.

Slowly open your eyes.

If you find this process too difficult to start with, practice while resting on the bed or floor. When we prepare for sleep the body will automatically adopt abdominal breathing as this is your natural breathing pattern. Relax and simply observe the movement with hands resting as described above, then gently, actively participate in the movement.

Cyclic Breath

Cyclic breathing supports the development of calm breathing and is an excellent way to maximise both the amount of energy being absorbed into the body and the toxic cells being released out of it. This is achieved by pausing gently between the inbreath and the out and then the outbreath and the in. This allows the membrain around the lungs to absorb healthy levels of energy and have time to then transfer the carbonated dead cells and excess moisture into the lungs to be expelled on the out breath.

The gentle pause between the out breath and the in breath is the time of pure tranquility, where the body and mind are at total stillness. During practice you may find this time will naturally lenghten as your Prana levels rise and your body is no longer in a state of panic. Your sense of calm and peace will increase with practice.

Steps: -

Find your seat and ensure the body is fully supported by the spine.

Relax the jaw and soften the tongue.

Close the eyes and turn the line of sight towards the middle of the eyebrows. (You may feel a bit cross-eyed)

Relax the fingers and allow the hands to rest gently on the thighs.

Sink the tailbone gently into the chair on the outbreath.

Become aware of the natural movement of the body and allow the breath to relax into abdominal breathing. Spend time doing this until it becomes natural, calm and relaxed.

Visualize a rectangular box, possibly a door frame, and take the line of vision to the bottom left-hand corner.

Using abdominal breathing, gently breathe in

to the count of 4 (without tightening the chest), moving the eyes up the side of the box.

Pausing on the inbreath, travel across the top for the count of 2.

Descend the right side, breathing out to the count of 4-5.

Pause after the outbreath for the count of 2 and to the start.

Repeat the action until the breath becomes natural.

Continue for up to 5 minutes.

If your breathing becomes forced, allow yourself to go back to natural breath and restart the cyclic breathing when ready.

Positive Affirmations

Steps: -

The use of positive phrases while breathing will assist you in cementing your conscious and subconscious mind's new positive attitudes and standards.

Find your seat and release the muscles in the body to allow you to sit upright, supported by the spine.

Close the eyes, release the jaw and loosen the tongue, then begin by relaxing the chest and engaging abdominal breath.

Once comfortable, move into cyclic breath using the 4:2:4:2 process detailed above.

Continue for a few minutes until the breathing becomes natural and relaxed. Keep your eyes closed and turned up to centre of the brow.

First affirmation: in your mind say "SLOW" on the inbreath and "DOWN" on outbreath. Continue for 1-2 minutes or until the sounds become natural within the breath.

Slowing down the breath to a ratio of 6:2:6:2

Second affirmation: in your mind say "I am calm" on the in breath and "I am relaxed" on the outbreath.

Continue for a few minutes until the breath becomes natural then return to natural breath for a few minutes.

Slowly open your eyes as you take a long in breath.

Channel Cleansing Breath

<u>Balancing your YIN and YANG in the Mind</u>

Channel Cleansing supports the balancing of both sides of the mind by consciously breathing through one nostril then the other.

Steps: -

Assume your position and spend a few moments to relax the neck and shoulders, release the lower back and allow the spine to realign to support the body.

Close the eyes, gently turning the eyes upwards, loosen the jaw and allow the tongue to rest at the bottom of the mouth.

Relax your hands and place the left comfortably on the thigh, palm facing upwards. Fold the index and middle finger of the right hand down towards the palm to allow the use of the ring finger and thumb. Gently place the ring finger over the left nostril, closing off the air supply.

Inhale slowly and calmly, through the right nostril, breathing using abdominal breath, to a slow count of 3-6 (depending on your personal level of attainment). Once you have naturally inhaled *without* strain, hold the breath in the body for a count of 3.

Close the right nostril with the thumb and gently release the left and allow the outbreath to exit the body calmly and slowly, again without strain with the same count.

Keeping the left nostril open, breathe in through the left to a slow count of 3-6, pause, and then exhale through the right with the same count.

This is one complete cycle, which should be completed a minimum of 3 times and a maximum of 9, then simply release the hand and return to normal breath.

In Summary

By now you will be aware that regaining health, balance and roots will take time, patience, a development of personal fortitude and self-examination. It will not happen overnight but when you, and the people around you, start to notice changes, these changes will become significant in your life. Each step you take becomes a little stronger and a little bolder until the baby-step full of dread and fear becomes a determined stride, powerful and full of the confidence that you are worth investing in.

Discovering your path, your passion for living, is the most rewarding thing you can ever do, both for yourself and your loved ones. Creating strong foundations for life, setting out parameters for what is acceptable to yourself and how you will project yourself out towards others will then reflect back on to you from the people around you through the laws of Karma.

Respect and love yourself unconditionally and you will gain respect and love from the world. Prepare for the road ahead. The old adage 'fail to plan – plan to fail' is true in every aspect of life. Plan to succeed. Plan to be happy.

Do not accept without question your self-imposed limiting beliefs of old. They have been the shackles which have held you back, possibly even made you ill, or made you feel small.

Visualize, with conviction, yourself happy, healthy and mentally strong and you will become so.

Reward yourself for positive actions and become your own best friend, full of encouragement and love.

When you find something hard, reassure yourself that you only need to find the answer.

Keep telling yourself that you are an amazing, strong individual and you can work through any challenge and be triumphant.

Remember:

Good yogis are not perfect human beings,

but people who have recognized their patterns

of suffering and are putting energy

into breaking through those patterns.

Take time to reflect on the relevance of having more energy in your life. What difference will having a clear mind and more vitality have on you and your loved ones?

Notes

Start Thinking about Thinking

Can you recall a moment recently where you wanted some space to think? When was it?

What influences prevented you from having that space?

How do you feel improving your head space will benefit you? What areas of your life will be affected?

List small things you can change today to enable you to move towards having that space.

1.

2.

3.

4.

5.

Growing your Wings

(Rediscover peace)

Dear Reader,

Developing spiritually (and by this, I mean becoming the truest version of yourself) is a very personal journey. No one path is the same so I can only give you simple guidance as my path will not be the same as yours. Just as each one of us is unique in our traits, personality and life lesson, we must find our own way to happiness and fulfilment in our path.

The next part of your journey is truly the most rewarding.

You can begin to change past negative Karma into a positive experience and make real changes to your direction.

Try to regard your situation impartially and without emotional attachment, ask yourself the following questions when life is not going the way you 'want' it to.

"What can I learn from this experience?"

"Why has this happened, and what is the universe telling me?"

"How can I make this experience a positive one to complete this particular life lesson and move forward from it?"

"How can I make this life lesson useful to others and so support my cycle of positive Karma?"

To be able to do this you must first change the direction of your senses from being externally driven, seeking approval, to one of internal observation, knowing what is right for you, and build concentration within yourself. You will then become aware of, appreciate and engage better with other souls around you who are here to help and guide you to develop and learn.

Everyone you meet in your life is there deliberately, sent to give you help on your life journey. Some encounters may be hard experiences and some good, but each one will make you grow as a person if you look at it correctly, building your stamina and determination to succeed on your journey. Take each event that happens in life in good faith and consider the purpose of people entering your life, even if it is just to say hello when you are low.

When you are able to do this, you will be truly learning and positively engaging in your life, no longer a spectator on the sidelines.

The path so far has set the foundations, the roots for your onward journey of self-discovery.

Good luck moving forward

Introduction

The first four sections of this book have offered support in your first stages of change and by now you have hopefully gained a new sense of positive qualities to observe in your own behavior and what you will accept from others.

In sections one and two, you looked at the initial aim of being non-violent and truthful to others. Not stealing their time or energy and being content with your own life will help you feel grounded. So, with the added benefits of eating natural foods, a personal commitment to be happy and develop your true-self, life begins to be a happier and more pleasant place to be. All of this takes time, so don't feel you need to change completely and all at once. Instead, allow yourself to relax and take time to get to know and appreciate subtle changes. Allow your principles to grow organically, naturally unfolding and growing steadily stronger.

In section three, you have hopefully gained a better understanding of why you need a relaxed, strong and healthy body for your soul to reside and develop in. You know why you need to breathe well to draw in health-giving Prana to support your mind and emotions, as well as oxygenating the physical body to improve cell regeneration. Once you have strong and steady foundations, a naturally healthy body with a solid moral code, you can grow emotionally and mentally, secure in the knowledge that you are safe and grounded.

In section four, you have looked at the benefits of breathing well and evaluated your life 'battery' and established a more sustainable way of stopping the drain on your energy, learning how to build a healthier reserve of Prana.

Visualize your mind as the conductor of a great orchestra: you have learned about the instruments and what they do, you have placed them in the correct position to get the best results without conflict or force, and now it is time to take control and learn how to create wonderful music.

It is important to remember that the physical form and the harmonizing of Prana to energize your life needs constant attention and development. Regular yoga classes or Bhakti (devotional) groups are vital to keep you moving forward naturally. Your body is continuously changing, creating new, healthier cells and gaining strength every day but you need to keep your focus on it. If you start to neglect your physical form or stop reaffirming your breathing techniques, the body will become lazy again and you will start to drop back into old habits. As already stated, you need to follow the correct processes and create life-long positive habits to enable the soul to grow and strengthen. Have a start, a middle, and an end to every choice you make as if you give up half way through, you do not complete the cycle of energy and create positive Karma (The Path of Action). Every choice you make will come back around. What you put out comes back in.

If you give up on life, life gives up on you.

So, do not give up on anything, see everything through to its natural conclusion, even if the result is not what you were hoping for. This is a life lesson, and if you complete your tasks, life will reward you. Remember that the easiest route is not always the right one for you to take and forbearance (one of your personal commitments) will build resilience. The next two sections will help to fortify your sense of peace and happiness while creating achievable goals in life.

Limb 5 and limb 6 – Pratyahara and Dharana

Limb 5, known as the gateway to your higher self, supports the withdrawal from external referencing and draws the senses inwards by developing focus.

Limb 6 is the building of concentration within the mind, it supports the steadying of your consciousness by embracing the senses and observing and reflecting on your actions as a third party. When Pratyahara and Dharana are combined, they create the fortification of your will power and the manifestation of your goals in life.

5. Pratyahara

Withdrawal of the External Influences, or Senses

(The bridge between your physical life and your soul)

There are three parts to this limb, which require cultivation over a long period of time, patience and the removal of 'trying' or 'searching' outwardly to achieve. Instead, allow a sense of stillness to develop and so enable enlightenment to naturally come to you, unfolding in its own time, in its true form. This part of your journey is truly inspiring and, if you allow it to develop organically, you will start to surprise yourself with a new sense of being and a new ability to hear what your heart (Soul) is guiding you towards.

Calming the Five Physical Senses

Taste – Begin to withdraw from over-flavored and unnaturally stimulating edible substances, such as processed foods, and explore new pleasures in simpler, 'real' foods, which nourish the body and calm the mind. Try preparing a meal full of naturally occurring colour and taste as each taste and colour have different life supporting elements.

Sugar is now probably the world's most problematic and addictive drug; it is everywhere, in most foods with a shelf life, and prepared drinks you buy. Sugar creates a craving within the body like heroin or cocaine, but unlike these drugs everyone *needs* food to live. So, the only way of getting off the drug called sugar is to eat natural foods, made from scratch. In addition to sugar, caffeine has been called the nation's drug of choice and figures show there is now one coffee shop to every two pubs in the UK, with numbers rising year on year.

You will need to slowly cut down the volume of sugary foods and caffeine you consume daily, as just like any drugs, you will hit a deep low in the short term if you cut them out cold turkey. Instead, take small steps towards achieving this; try changing to herbal teas instead of coffee and switch out biscuits for a piece of fruit.

Sight – The more stimulated you are through food and drink, the more alert the mind will become, and the eyes are then triggered to identify danger as the stress hormones in your body are on alert. Modern technology is fast and furious on the eyes. You speed-read through articles, looking at several devices at once, eyes darting from one thing to another, constantly searching, overstimulating the eyes and leaving little or no time to truly observe life or yourself.

To support your journey inwards, you need to calm the vision and allow the eyes to stop searching. Reduce artificial stimulation of TV, gaming, especially avoiding aggressive, disrespectful and violent scenes, which heighten your stress hormone levels. Place calming images in your home and workplace and spend as much time as possible out in nature. Switch off devices for half an hour before you go to bed in the evening and remove televisions from the bedroom.

Hearing – Too much noise can cause distress within the whole of the nervous system. Think back to a time when you have been in a very noisy venue and you can feel your heart pounding. This is because excess noise stimulates the 'fight or flight' system within you, heightening the senses. Choose calming and positive music which induces a sense of peace. Lower the sound levels on your devices and commit to spending time in silence, starting with just half an hour a day - the bath is a good place to start. Slowly spend more time doing quiet activities and enjoy the peace it gives you. This will support your preparation for meditation practice, too.

Smell – Artificially scented candles and room fresheners trick the mind and give false stimulation to the senses so open the windows to let nature freshen your room instead. Become aware of how clean your air is (remember, energy is only present in fresh air) and take steps to spend as much time as possible in this environment. Fresh air indicates to the mind that all is well, and it can relax.

Touch – Your skin is a living breathing organ, protecting the body and soul from external damage and one of the skin's duties is to act as the body's emergency exit point for releasing toxins. Spots or rashes can be a sign from the digestive system that what you have put into your body is not good for you. This is evident with the huge rise in allergies in the past 30 years and there is no surprise that this rise has coincided with the increase of processed foods containing chemicals, stabilizers and preservatives.

When your body becomes too hot, the skin releases the excess heat by means of sweat to cool the surface and when it gets too cold, it closes the pores to prevent heat loss (goose pimples).

In more extreme cases, when a foreign body such as poison or illness enters the body, heat levels within your body are naturally turned up and a fever occurs. This is to allow the body to burn off the bacteria and viruses that have entered (just like in cooking where you heat food to kill the bacteria). During the fever the body is operating its defense mechanism and as soon as the foreign body has been destroyed the temperature comes down. So, be wise when it comes to temperature in the body, sometimes it needs be allowed to kill bacteria itself, without drugs. (Obviously if you are concerned and feel ill always contact your GP or health professional straight away.)

To calm the sense of touch, focus on natural textiles to create a calmer sensation to the skin. Use only natural products on the skin to support its health and take care not put to the skin to extreme variances of external heat. Keep the skin clean and healthy, using only natural oils so as not to block its essential exit points (pores).

The sense of touch is also the main way to physically connect with another person, or soul. A handshake, a touch on the shoulder, or a loving embrace sends signals from one body to another, through the senses in the skin. This physical connection creates a subtle connection which induces a sense of calm and peace within the emotions. (We will discuss touch in more detail in a later section.)

The five senses are nature's gifts to the soul to connect with what is going on externally and to record your life journey, so keep your messages clear and true. For example, violent loud films can send a message of impending danger and ingredients which create a false taste can confuse the digestive system, thereby inflicting digestive ailments.

Confuse the senses with untruths and you will very quickly start to feel out of sync and anxious. Create the right environment and you will start to feel better straight away.

For example, think about how you feel emotionally and mentally when you are on holiday, resting on a beach on a gloriously sunny day, listening to the waves lap on the shore... you are calm and happy.

Think about how you feel emotionally and mentally when you are in a busy, noisy traffic jam in the centre of a crowded city, with petrol fumes coming into the car and the radio is playing a pounding bass track... you are anxious and unhappy.

Now, take yourself back to the picture of you being on a beach and feel your senses calming the physical body as well as relaxing your mind and emotions.

Take control and respect your senses, allow them to do their work correctly and effectively to help you stay happy and calm.

What small changes can you make in your everyday life to help support the calming of unnatural, external influences on of your senses?

Taste

Sight

Hearing

Smell

Touch

Mastering the Flow of Prana within the Subtle Body.

Prana (energy or vitality) flows through the body by means of a great network of nerves. However, as you are starting to appreciate, if left to run unchecked this can cause distress and dis-ease within the physical body, the emotional body, and most importantly, the mental/spiritual body.

So, mastering the flow of prana is essential. Too much can overstimulate the senses and take your consciousness back to external matters, engaging in ego-based activities. Too little prana slows the flow, creating blockages, a sense of stagnation and a low ability to function effectively.

You may be thinking at this point, *"Haven't we already spoken at great lengths about Prana?"*. The answer, of course, is yes, but you will find elements of all eight elements in each one of the sections, gently entwined. We talked about the importance of the lungs and the work they do to create new healthy cells through the Prana we breath in. We talked about the sources of Prana and how to build up your own daily store of energy to maintain a healthy physical form and then how to reduce the impact of energy thieves by not engaging and being drawn into their dramas. All of these processes calm the senses, build your personal store of energy, and support the development of your conscious commitment and direction of Prana towards spiritual evolution.

During this section we look at how to focus your Prana to withdraw from external influences on your physical body. Prana is then redirected into your energetic body to develop strength within the subtle body (your emotions and mind). This in turn fortifies your determination in life and your ability to move forward. In simpler terms, clearing physical distractions enables you to keep your energy levels high and your emotions balanced.

Conscious observational breathing should be part of your daily focus. Regularly checking in, scanning for feelings of stress, fatigue, stiffness or negativity, enables you to identify your triggers and begin to take positive steps to do something about them. Ensuring the breath is calm and long, absorbing a continuous flow of positive energy within the body, returns balance to your Yin and Yang.

Like the river which flows naturally within the boundaries of its banks, following a regulated course, our 'life force' needs direction, clear boundaries and room to flow. Happiness and joy can bring great amounts of energy but if you have no direction or commitment, our energy soon becomes stale and blocked up, coming to a standstill, just like a river full of rubbish and debris. So, energy begins to overflow, breaking its banks and boundaries, causing chaos. When your energies overflow due to lack of direction or commitment in life you feel out of control and cling to anything and everything, both emotionally and physically, to resist this sense of being swept away.

Creating direction for your energy is essential to drive your path forward and so it is time to start planning for your long-term happiness.

Like any worthwhile project, it needs to be well thought out, with realistic (but not limiting) goals, to give you the best chance to complete each cycle of Karma or task. Each time you complete a task you gain strength and become more immune to failure.

Start with small goals, but ones that require your commitment to a positive change. For example, giving up smoking, changing your job to a more spiritually rewarding one, improving your circle of friends and gently removing your emotional drains. Consider the following...

Redirecting the Energy Flow

Identify a situation that currently drains you emotionally.

How can you stem the drain of your energy with a positive change?

Identify a situation that currently drains you mentally.

How can you stem the drain of your energy with a positive change?

Now

Identify a situation that can refill you emotionally. What do you love to do?

Identify a situation that can refill you mentally. What stimulates you mentally?

<u>Begin to find ways to plug the leakage of your energy and begin to self-nourish.</u>

The Withdrawal of External Influence from the Mind.

The mind is an amazing tool but up to now in your life, it may well have spent most of its time in self-preservation or protection mode, keeping you safe from the perceived dangers simulated through modern life.

The modern epidemic of anxiety, depression, stress and anger can be classed as a fear of existence, as the protective mind begins to see everything as a potential threat. This is perpetuated every day in the violence seen on TV and on the internet, the news and radio. It effects how you speak to others and intensifies the limitations put upon you by yourself or people around you. Through this continual downward spiral of limiting emotions, you are creating your own jail. Karmically, if you put fear out into the world through thought, word or deed, you receive fear back in equal measures.

Stop and really think about this…

"All relationships are a reflection of your relationship with yourself."

For example, a person who feels fear or insecurity about money or success in life, be it spiritual or financial, is simply experiencing reflections of fear or insecurities about themselves. No amount of money or success will make them happy or resolve their fears, they must conquer their own personality first to be able to have real success.

Get to know yourself, develop your love for yourself and appreciate your beauty as this will bring about the personal healing you need to allow true happiness and success to flourish within you. Become your own best friend.

Spend time getting to know yourself through silent contemplation; open yourself up and gently and lovingly work through your unfinished business. Complete your old Karma. To move forward, you must first complete each life lesson, remember, there must be a beginning, middle and end to each event. We have put energy out into the universe with an action, so therefore, need to receive it back with a reaction. A completion. If you can change something for the good, then change it. If you cannot, accept it, let it go and move on. To complete old karma, good or bad, you need to either change the experience into good or let it go.

Do not judge yourself, instead, accept the past, make peace with previous unfinished life lessons and find ways to use these experiences to help others. This way you will never feel guilt, fear or insecurity again as you have connected with your positive and limitless life energy and potential. You will become your true self, the best version of yourself.

Make a commitment to become non-judgmental of others as this frees up a huge amount of your mental capacity for your own personal development. Why spend time criticizing and analyzing others when you could be using that time and energy developing and improving yourself? Invest in yourself. Spend time developing positive Karma by acknowledging your three centres of reference.

Your Spiritual Centre is the mind, using acquired knowledge to make decisions. Up to now it has been programmed through fear and through external influences, needing constant approval from others and recognition for its actions. It has become the ego. Initially it cannot be trusted to give you a true reflection of what is happening and so you need to spend time to calm and support it to change through your breathing and focused practice.

Your Self Centre is the solar plexus, your survival instinct and natural reaction, the gut instinct. Nature has given the Soul (you) chemical reactions within the body to identify whether a situation is good or bad, creating a feeling of comfort (excitement) or discomfort (dread) within the gut. However, just like the spiritual centre, the gut has been programmed through fear and has lost the ability (for now) to distinguish between the two. It therefore defaults to self-preservation, making every situation discomfort and limiting the expansion of the soul. This default self-preservation mode will prevent you from putting yourself forward into potential danger, thus you are held in a self-imposed safety zone.

When you begin asking for help within, and require a true answer, ask the Heart Centre. Your Heart Centre is your true self and will never lie. Ask for support when you need to make a decision, then wait for the answer. Remember, your Heart has also been neglected and may have become quiet, fearful and unwilling to speak out. So, keep asking with the true intention of obtaining a real response, then you will start to hear a quiet voice in the background, a *feeling* about something. This is your true self giving you guidance, it is then up to you to act upon it. For the Heart to grow in courage, it must be listened to and its advice acted upon. If you ignore its messages, it will once again become quiet and its guidance will be lost to you.

However, following your Heart Centre can often be a very difficult thing to do, as the answers you get may not be simple to follow or easy to accept. You may have to ask further questions of your Heart Centre before you come to a true answer. You may initially find that during this process you do not like what you see in yourself or others. You will begin to see your energy drains more clearly and will then need to make a choice over what to do about them.

Slowly, over time, the Spiritual Centre will begin to use its intelligence more wisely; with the support of calm senses and without self-limiting emotional interference, it will develop rational thinking. It will then liase with the Self Centre to distinguish effectively between comfort and discomfort, raising confidence to act. The mind and instinct working together will eventually bring balance to the Heart.

Intelligence of the mind + Instinct of the gut = Intuition of the heart.

Intuition of the heart creates the right response to every situation, known as the Spontaneous Right Action. When your mind, gut and Heart are all balanced and working effectively, you will naturally do the right thing for yourself and the people around you. Your conscience is clear, and you create comfort in your body, mind and Heart.

This state of being creates a sense of 'ease' within the body and so removes 'dis-ease' in the form of physical ailments. Tension within the body caused by doing the wrong thing can make you physically ill. You can therefore improve your physical health as well as your emotional, mental and spiritual health by balancing your three centres.

As a side benefit, you are also improving the environment in which you are living. Your family and people around you will be happier, your home will be cleaner and brighter as you will take more pride in it, and you will be more conscious of your behavior towards others.

Your Heart will always give you the right answer as it is honest, rational and intuitive. It is centered. Trust in it and spend time and energy on what is important, who you really are. By doing so, you will slowly steady the mind and gut.

Imagine the Heart as a parent with two totally different children, both wanting to explore life with different traits and qualities. The Mind is a dominant child who stamps their feet and demands you listen to them and carry out their whims. The Self is a quiet, patient child whose needs can sometimes be overlooked due to the demands of the first child. Each one is unique and wonderful in their own right and each has great potential to thrive and expand. Your role, as the mother (Heart), is to give them guidance, love and encouragement, work to their strengths and support their weaknesses.

The Mind – Spend time and energy bringing discipline into your thoughts and processes of thinking. When your mind wanders, or your imagination gets the better of you in situations, you need to take charge and kindly but firmly say, "*I am not engaging with this right now, I will come back to it when I am ready*".

Spend time considering every thought and action and become more proactive, rather than reactive, by instigating the 'deferred pleasure principle': instead of indulging in a cheap thought or fancy, or engaging in other people's dramas, criticism or negativity, choose the opposite action and your reward (Karma) will be a moment of liberation, of freedom.

The Self (gut) – Spend time and energy giving unconditional love and attention to yourself. Your gut is you: your confidence, your self-esteem, your stamina to fully engage in life. To build confidence in your abilities you need to change the way you speak to yourself by becoming your own best friend.

Changing Vocabulary

Limiting self-belief holds you back from your true greatness, by talking yourself out of taking risks as it is "SAFER" not to, either physically or emotionally. You worry about the consequences of your actions so much that, eventually, you end up doing nothing, and life becomes stagnant. The gut has learned not to trust your opinion and has convinced itself you are not worthy of happiness. You may have developed habits of putting yourself down, "you are not good enough", "you are stupid", "you will be laughed at".

As well as restricting our lives, this behavior can have a profound effect on the people around us. In addition to their meaning, our words, both spoken and written, also carry energy from ourselves to their recipient. Whichever way we communicate, each word has a life of its own, a vibratory signature that creates waves in the same way as music. The tone and emotion of the spoken word can create vibrations of positivity or negativity, affecting the people around us accordingly. When we are conscious of the energy behind our words, we become capable of making a real positive difference to the world, but when we are not conscious of the power of words, we run the risk of creating disturbances, fear and negativity.

Some of us know this instinctively, while others come to this understanding slowly and over time. Most of us, though, speak without thinking at least some of the time, blurting out our feelings and thoughts without regard for the words we choose to express them. When we remind ourselves that our words have an impact on the world at the level of energy, we can begin to increase our desire to be more aware of our language.

Consider who you are speaking to and create the right level of energy. For example, a baby in a cot would be spoken to with a different energy to your boss at work. Make small changes to your thought patterns and have courage to take gentle steps each day. You will begin to see big positive changes occurring naturally. Start with your vocabulary to yourself.

Make a list of the negative vocabulary you currently use to yourself and to others and consider the energetic vibration it creates.

Word   Energetic Vibration

A fun way to increase your sensitivity to the power of words is to convert your negative words to positive ones and notice the subtle change in your mind and emotions. And don't forget to smile when you say them!

Negative emotional words	Positive Transformation
Angry	Disenchanted
Afraid	Uncomfortable
Anxious	Expectant
Confused	Curious
Depressed	On the road to a turn around
Destroyed	Set back
Disgusted	Surprised
Dread	Challenge
Exhausted	Recharging
Failure	Getting educated
Furious	Passionate
Impatient	Anticipating
Irritated	Stimulated
Jealous	Over loving
Lazy	storing energy
Lonely	Available
Overwhelmed	Maximized
Rejected	Available
Scared	Excited
Sick	Cleansing
Stressed	Busy
Stupid	Discovering
Terrible	Different

Changing You, Changing Others

What is your most recent experience of speaking negatively to yourself?

Why did it happen and how did it make you feel afterwards?

If the situation had happened to your best friend, how would you have approached this differently? What positive suggestions could you have offered?

Choose one thing about your behavior towards yourself that you would really like to change and describe it. How would that manifest itself positively and what difference would it make to you and the people around you?

Make a list of small things you can start doing today to help you make this happen:

1.

2.

3.

4.

5.

159

Notes

6. Dharana

Building Concentration

As you have travelled along your journey so far, you have gained your roots and, through good breathing habits, you have developed the bridge between the physical body and the spiritual one, understanding the need to calm the five physical senses. You have removed unnatural stimuli, developed Prana functions to create positive commitment and focus on your life path. Lastly, you have recreated a connection between the three main energy centres, harmonizing the mind, the gut instinct and the Heart so that you can *hear* your true self's directions.

By engaging wholeheartedly in inward reflection rather than outward approval, you give your soul permission to develop, starting to see your life potential and open yourself to new experiences and learning opportunities. As you focus, the mind slows down, you become more attentive and relaxed, allowing other thoughts to slip away. This will not be easy, especially at first, and it will take longer for some people than others.

This is not meditation. It is the development of the *immovable concentration of the mind.*

By developing concentration, you are creating the right conditions for the mind to focus on the current situation and be present, instead of jumping from one thought to the next, from the past to the future. With regular practice, this concentration will expand out into many aspects of your life and become part of your everyday experiences, releasing endorphins (happy hormones) into the body so you feel more relaxed.

As concentration levels extend and the mind and soul become more harmonized, external chatter quietens, physical discomfort within the body subsides and, before you know it, you will find yourself sitting quietly and peacefully for a long period of time, focused on your activity.

The basic instructions are:

Create a positive, fresh and clean environment for your practice to allow the mind to calm. Physically relax the body, completing gentle stress-releasing movements learnt in your Asana practice. Calm the breathing by using methods learnt in Pranayama.

Choose one thing to focus on (your BHAKTI practice) and explore it.

When your mind wanders, accept it but always bring it back to your activity (complete your action/Karma).

Leave everything else at the door.

After a few minutes of focus, it is natural for the mind to try and distract you. After all, it is the mind's job to analyze things and, to the overactive mind, being quiet is boring. By adopting the *'deferred pleasure principle'*, dropping that distracting thought and returning to your chosen point of focus, you are doing something wonderful - you are proactively taking back control of your mind and thoughts and creating discipline within yourself.

Over a period, the 'monkey mind', full of chatter and noise, will learn to be obedient and not interrupt you while you are focusing on your point of concentration, and your mind will clear with a greater capacity for insight.

Focusing, however, does not mean blocking everything else out, this is impossible. Instead, it is more like operating a camera lens, as you gently zoom into your chosen topic, it becomes much clearer. The background is still there, and you are aware of it, but it is out of focus and incidental, in your peripheral vision.

Personal Reflection

This time on your path will be one of personal observations as well as retraining your mind. You will have more quiet time to allow your soul to revisit issues and memories which have been locked away in the darkest recesses of your mind. Perhaps you have been too scared to deal with them and over time they may have begun to weigh you down.

Take a moment to appreciate every event that you have not yet resolved or brought to its natural conclusion by completing your circle of energy (Karma). Take time to understand that every emotion, which has manifested itself into a self-limiting belief, has a physical form and therefore a physical weight attached to it. Understand that you can become physically weighed down with worry, sadness or past events, unable to move forward with your life as you remain shackled to your past.

As stated earlier, the brain cannot complete its task of analyzing and evaluating, and subsequently closing each chapter, unless there is a beginning, a middle and an *end*. If there is no conclusion to the task, the imagination will begin to create possible endings of its own: good, bad, sad, happy, even bizarre, just to finish the story. The mind will repeat a situation over and over, becoming more intense as the brain desperately tries to resolve the issue for you.

It is no wonder, then, that in times of trouble in your life, when you are faced with a situation that seems too difficult to face, your mind plays the scenario on constant repeat; replaying it with, 'I should have said this', 'I could have done that', 'what if' etc. In extreme cases, the brain will often create a whole new memory of the situation just to find a resolution. In the rewritten version of the story, you will be justified in your actions, you'll be the hero of the piece, giving you a sense of triumph and satisfaction. Or, adversely, justify your fears, creating you as the victim, badly done to and reaffirming your reasoning to remain in your mental safe place. The brain does this as a form of self-preservation, like opening a release valve, which reduces the extreme pressure on the emotions and allows them to subside, thus concluding the event. This is known as a false memory.

You can compare the mind, with its many unresolved events (stories), to a computer, where the user has opened lots of different programs, which are all running at the same time. You know what happens... the computer gets slower and slower until, eventually, the whole thing crashes.

Use your time to attend to each story as it comes to you for resolution and finish it by using your third Niyama principle of inner development – forbearance.

<u>What you can change for the good:</u> Take courage and finish each story to its full conclusion and with a real positive outcome. Listen to your heart and ask it what you should do, especially when it means taking responsibility for personal failure. Liberate yourself.

<u>What you cannot do anything about:</u> Accept these things and the important life lessons they offer with good grace and without judgement or prejudice to yourself or others. Learn from each one and then move on.

Every moment of every day, you are making choices. You choose to get up, or not. You choose whether to nourish your body by eating a healthy breakfast, or rush straight out to work. You choose to be kind, or cruel. *Everything* that has happened in your life up to now you have chosen, either by active participation or simply by allowing events to happen. When you accept that your decisions and actions in the past have brought you to this place in your life and made you the person you are today, with all your metaphorical bumps and bruises, you will be in control of your future.

Standing in judgement of yourself and others will not allow you to grow as a person and move forward in your life as it creates turbulence both within yourself and the world around you. The constant labelling of things as being right or wrong, good or bad, creates a constant flow of evaluation, classification and analysis throughout your day. This distracts you from your purpose and depletes your energy levels and time, until you become exhausted.

Conversely, by taking control and being non-judgmental, you will create space and silence within the mind, giving it room to relax, and begin to move you forward with conscious awareness.

Every action generates a force of energy that returns to us in like kind.

What we sow is what we reap.

When we chose actions that bring happiness and success to others, the fruit of Karma is happiness and success in ourselves.

To change negative past Karma into a positive experience you need to ask yourself four questions:

What can I learn from this experience?

Why has this happened to me at this time in my life?

What message is being sent to me? (What Karma needs to be repaid?)

How can I make this experience a positive one and make it useful to others?

Then and only then can you create your own upward cycle of Karma.

Every story or action (Karma) you complete, do it with love and compassion, and without judgement. It will then become a positive life experience, which you can use for the good, rather than a negative experience, which has held you back, restricting your energy and true potential. Every program you close on your brain computer will make you think more effectively and clearly, you will begin to feel physically lighter as you cut these ties to your old baggage.

Many of the life stories that you have been unable or unwilling to finish will need some self-reflection and acceptance. *You* are the architect of your life so far. *You* have been responsible for every action, choice and decision in your life, good or bad. You will learn a lot about yourself and how you have treated others in the past and will be required to change or, as yogic teaching believes, *evolve* into the best person you can and, most importantly, *should* be.

Accept your past personal failings and resolve to be a better person. This choice will liberate you physically, emotionally and spiritually. It is good to make mistakes as long as you learn positive lessons from them and grow as a person. Modern western society fears making mistakes, instead, everybody strives for perfection. But without mistakes, how can you learn?

How can you build resilience?

How can you thrive?

A life spent making and learning from mistakes is a true life.

"True Yoga is not about the shape of your body,

But the shape of your life.

Yoga is not to be performed;

Yoga is to be lived.

Yoga does not care what you have been,

Yoga cares about the person you are becoming.

Yoga is designed for a vast and profound purpose

And for it to be truly called Yoga, its essence must be embedded."

The fire of Love

By Aadil Palkhivala

Developing your focus and concentration is not all about serious matters; it's important on your journey of self-discovery, and cultivation of self-love and appreciation, to get involved in things which really make your heart sing. You will then perform your concentration out of love and joy rather than a sense of duty or obligation.

Mind and Body in Harmony = Contented Soul (Heart)

Get involved in some of the following activities to support balance in your Heart.

Cooking	Reading a book	Knitting
Sewing	Card-making	Gardening
Painting	Model-making	Singing
Weaving	Walking groups	Golf
Exercise class	Woodwork	Crosswords
Cross stitch		

These are just a few examples; the list of possibilities is endless.

Make a list of activities you would like to get involved in.

Getting involved in traditional activities, which support your learning and improve your patience, will create a sense of calm within the body. By encouraging the mind and the physical body to work cooperatively together in an activity, the Heart becomes balanced and happy. Learning a new skill requires patience, gives you a great sense of achievement and a deeper connection to yourself. Importantly, the activity of learning a new skill also contains within it a clear start, middle and end and so strengthens the ability to complete the cycle of Karma and build resilience in life.

Concentration skills are a prerequisite for your development into Meditation. However, continuous concentration is very difficult to maintain without aids because of all the external and internal distractions modern life throws at you.

When you relax to do your seated session, it is possible that you may relax too much and fall asleep. This is ok as your body obviously needed this rest, but as you continue on your meditation journey, the dilemma becomes:

If you try too hard to concentrate and not fall asleep, you may end up with mental strain.

If you try not to concentrate and relax too much you end up with all the above pitfalls anyway

Mala beads are an excellent tool to support you in this transition as they help you to focus your attention without strain.

Mala Beads (Japa Dharana)

Japa means 'to rotate' and Dharana means 'concentration', therefore we can say that Mala Beads are used for 'rotating concentration'.

Mala beads are a string of 108 beads (there are shorter ones available at 54 and 27) with the additional, larger bead called the Sumeru, which connects both ends with a knot. 'Sumeru' means junction or summit and is significant in the support of the user's concentration as a reference point to confirm they have completed 108 repetitions. It is stated that this is the number required to reach your higher self's consciousness. So, if you have a string of 54 beads, you repeat the cycle twice, and so on.

When Mala beads are not being used for concentration purposes, they are often used as a necklace to help subconsciously reaffirm your intention and give gentle reassurance to the wearer that you are ok.

Positive affirmations will continue to be an important practice in your development of concentration. As your conscious breathing techniques become well established and part of the natural rhythm of your day, you will find they will also become the cornerstone of your sense of stillness and calm during meditation.

Choosing positive words to direct through the body, or simply observing the motion of the breath are excellent tools to support your Dharana (concentration) practice.

Practice:

Relax the body using gentle stretches to release physical tension before assuming your preferred position for practice.

Place the string of Mala beads over the middle two fingers of your right hand holding the first bead in between the thumb and the ring finger. The Sumaru should be facing downward.

Take time to calm the senses and bring your awareness inwards.

Rotate the bead in between your thumb and ring finger while stating your mantra, gently synchronizing it with the breath.

Move the thumb to middle finger and draw the next bead down to ring finger.

Repeat the mantra while rotating the bead.

During this period of new-found peace and contentment, emotional and mental strength will begin to grow, and a new sense of stillness will develop within you.

Your Yama and Niyama (observations to others and yourself) will naturally become entwined in the fabric of your life.

You will become more honest in word and deed to the people around you.

You will no longer feel anger or violence in action, word or even thought. Instead, you will become accepting.

You will feel full of energy and you will gain the ability to self-nourish, removing yourself from the negative cycles of energy-stealing and fighting for attention. Instead, you will willingly give love and support out to others.

You will become a radiator of energy.

You will find that people enjoy being around you and will gravitate towards you.

Your eating habits will become simpler as you start to eat for nourishment of the body, rather than to satisfy cravings, or fill emotional gaps.

Your life will take on a sense of calm and clarity. Your attention will be wholeheartedly on maintaining the lightness you feel in your Heart and Soul.

You will realise that it is possible for you to be happy, truly happy, in yourself and who you are.

You will be confident in your ability to make decisions, without reference back to your drains, and you will be ready to take responsibility for the outcomes of each choice you make.

You are now in control of your life.

It is time to start *really* living.

Today

I close the door on my past

Open the door to my future

Step through

And start a new chapter of my life

7. Dyana

Meditation

Everyday lifestyles are usually lived in a 'waking dream' state. Rather than being truly aware and attentive, living in the moment and being mindful, most people spend their day rolling from one emotionally charged thought to another: assuming, anticipating, regretting, fearing every moment. The whole day is consumed by rolling back over past events and the emotions attached to them or worrying about what will happen in the future.

If something unexpected happens to jolt you out of this state, perhaps the loss of a loved one, a serious accident, a divorce, or finding yourself out of work, you experience a major shift in your consciousness. Events such as these can cause you to feel as if you have suddenly woken up. In this one moment, your life flashes in front of your eyes and you see, with absolute clarity, what has been happening as you sleepwalked through it. As painful and shocking as these situations may be, they often cause you to feel truly awake and alive for the first time.

When tragedy strikes, your priorities change dramatically. What seemed very important before, like the fancy house and fast car, the latest trends and how many followers you have on Facebook, become insignificant and very often result in the questions:

'What is the meaning of my life?'

'What should I be doing with my life?'

In answering these questions, you may come to the realisation that life is too short to waste.

As we get older, we naturally move closer to our own deaths. As a result of this, many people experience a 'mid-life crisis', when they suddenly wake up to the fact that at 40, 50, 60, they have not done any of the things they dreamt about in their earlier years. The fear of death becomes overwhelming. Most people have heard of someone who has had a dramatic change in lifestyle or sold everything they own, maybe leaving a fabulous job and going off travelling to see the world without a backward glance. This is sometimes described as a mid-life crisis or as their awakening.

There are millions of books on how to meditate your way out of this dreamlike state. These books say it is the conscious state of meditation that leads to relaxation, concentration, awareness, peace, and contentment; that through meditation you can probe your thoughts and ideas more deeply and create what you want in your life. However, this approach has no depth and is only temporary.

Yogic philosophy believes in the development of a relaxed healthy body (Asana) while coming to terms with your past actions and finding peace and contentment through following the principles of Yama and Niyama. It believes in the development of your breath through Pranayama, allowing the mind to calm and improve focus and concentration through discipline and self-reflection. Only when you respect and honor yourself for the unique soul you are and offer peace to the world with your Heart's actions, thoughts and words, will you find contentment. These actions lead you to a state of Meditation.

Meditation is the state of absorption into true happiness and peace.

It is, in fact, impossible to teach meditation. It is only possible to teach the method that will lead to the experience of meditation. During the previous chapters, the knowledge you have gained supports that teaching. Remember this important point

Meditation is unteachable by the very fact that it is beyond the spoken word.

It is a unique experience to you.

Many people sit down, close their eyes for some time and consider that they have meditated. However, more often than not, they have only brooded over problems and thoughts of external influences while in the so-called state of meditation. Without introspection of the mind this is simply remaining external with your eyes closed and is not true Meditation.

Because true Meditation cannot be explained by logical references, its meaning and purposes have become diluted and deformed over the years to fit within the frameworks of externalized life traits – to suit the ego. Many people are not ready to look at themselves differently, they want to believe that their externalized lives are more important and satisfying than that of their soul. They want a quick fix, to play the part, rather than experience their lives through the hard work and self-reflection needed to get to this point in the journey. This has, therefore, narrowed most people's expectations and understanding of what meditation really is: it has become a physical entity in the eyes of the general populous, rather than a state of being and a way of living every day.

Meditation, like all aspects of yoga, is individual to each person, to each life journey and so there is no set path, nor correct process. The aim, however remains the same, to induce the spontaneous state of Meditation, or introspection; to generate within you a sense of joy at just being, while experiencing the greatest pleasure, respect and contentment in every aspect in your life.

Types of Meditation

Just like there are many styles of yoga practice, there are many styles of meditation practice.

Raja Meditation – The Path of Introspection. This is traditionally performed sitting in a quiet place with eyes closed and performing various practices to induce meditation. This is the most common style of meditation and is the most widely emulated throughout the world. Raja meditation offers time to reflect and observe life, while becoming aware of how your actions impact your life, through the stillness of the physical body.

Karma Meditation – The Path of Action. Through the yogic route it is possible to be in a state of meditation while performing everyday activities. Doing work, making dinner, driving your car - these can all be forms of meditation when done with awareness and loving intentions. If you consciously and purposely put out loving energy into the world and perform your task with the best intention, you receive the same quantity of love and peace back into your life. In order to improve the sense of love and peace that you experience, you must first give out love and peace.

Bhakti Meditation – The Path of Devotion. To spend your time and energy focusing on the pursuit and perfection of your chosen love (as discussed in 'Building your Concentration'). This would traditionally be a deity or a guru but can also be a craft, the evolution of spiritual worship/personal beliefs, or singing. Zen Buddhist monks spend their whole lives in the pursuit of perfection in one chosen thing (it may be gardening, cooking or a musical instrument, for example) as a way of devotion. They devote their time and energy to becoming the best person they can be by creating beauty for others to enjoy. This action of selflessness is the antidote to selfishness as you put someone or something before your own wants.

Hatha Meditation – The Path of Balance. This is the pursuit of harmony and balance within your life; getting the correct level of Yang (active) and Yin (passive) within your daily activities; being aware and conscious of how you feel within your body, that there is healthy energy flowing through your healthy temple. Hatha Meditation is your commitment to your Soul: honour your body with nourishing foods, sleep when tired, and maintain your Centre.

Jnana Meditation – The Path of Enquiry. As your body and mind reaches balance and perfection in concentration, your ability to *know* with absolute clarity, opens and expands your appreciation, acceptance and wonder of the world. Higher awareness cannot arise through rational thinking. Therefore, the final path of Jnana meditation is the path towards illuminative knowledge, which is neither logical nor illogical. This path is the opening, or illuminating, of the essence of existence and your true nature. By illumination, we do not mean stereotyped answers but *intuitive* answers, which you simply do not feel the need to speak of - if you *can* speak about it, it probably hasn't happened. As stated previously, many yogis do not speak of their higher experiences: they know it is impossible. Jnana meditation is open to everyone, but few people are ready for it. As your life evolves, and you follow your true path, you will begin to feel the gentle opening of this state. You will just know if something is right or wrong, good or bad, taking you forward or holding you back. You will develop the ability to make spontaneous right decisions, seamlessly improving your life.

Simply put, a person can perform the most trivial actions and yet simultaneously be in the highest stages of exultation, the experience of pleasure – the state of meditation. He can cut the lawn, drive a car, wash the dishes and at the same time be in a state of meditation, and probably no one else will know.

An ancient Zen master, Chikan, wrote the following:

"Pursuing the tasks of everyday life

I walk along the ancient path.

I am not disheartened in the mindless void"

Remember that there are different paths to meditation, just like there are different paths to yoga. Some involve outward actions, some involve inward contemplation. However, *all* involve being mentally in the same place as your physical body and loving each moment. Meditation is liberation from imposed restraints and enlightenment to the joy that every moment of life can bring, if you let it. Meditation is enhanced energy, which allows you to move forward in life with natural unwavering courage and clarity. Meditation is you at your absolute best.

Swami Sivananda was a firm believer in what he called 'integral yoga', in which all aspects of our personality are channeled through a combination of these different paths. He said that one should "Serve, Love, Give, Meditate, Realise". This encompasses the different aspects of action, devotion, introspection, benevolence and enquiry - the five paths of yoga. *This* is true yoga.

Yoga is the ability to live life truly, with compassion, courage and insight. Once you have opened this gift, which is waiting within you, you will never experience fear or pain. Instead, your life will be full of strength and courage for your journey ahead and your soul will thrive.

This is BLISS.

This is Samadhi.

This is the eighth limb.

This is the beginning of open joy in your long and vital life.

This is meditation in every moment of your life.

This is the beginning of your personal path, your adventure, your true self.

Notes

8 Samadhi – Bliss

Samadhi is the highest of all eight limbs and like the blossom tree it continues, year by year, to grow stronger and more beautiful. As your foundations and observations become more rooted in your world, and your personal conviction grows, you will become physically healthier and stronger; your heart will grow with the expansion of the loving energy, which flows outward into the world and back in from positive Karma; your mind will build resilience, stopping external influences from warping your sense of right and wrong, and creating space for your life to become exciting and full of adventure; and you will become courageous and steadfast as you make your way down your path in life. By keeping your roots well-nourished your branches will spread and expand.

A State of Samadhi is Juana yoga at its finest, bringing illumination into every part of your life and with it, intuition; a sense of 'just knowing' what to do, how to do it, and when to do it. Samadhi cannot be put into words because it is yours and yours alone. Every person's Samadhi is unique to them, to their life lesson and their journey. *You* will truly know when it happens, for life will become blissful and full of joy, and you will be able to live it peacefully with a sense of true belonging, and without the need to justify your actions or seek approval. When you experience a feeling of inexpressible *rightness (just knowing)*, you are experiencing Juana.

At the very outset of this book we noted that every living creature on this earth is here for a specific reason and has a purpose for being. As part of your journey back to living life as your authentic self it is vital that you open your mind to self-reflection and trusting your gut instinct. Be assured in the knowledge that you know your heart and path in life better than anyone and that it is your duty to follow where it leads.

If your life is not following your purpose you will never be truly happy, you will always feel unsettled and challenged. When life becomes a struggle and a feeling of being overwhelmed builds in the physical body and the mind, these questions and statements are often stimulated from the Heart:

"Why am I doing this?"

"I have no direction in my life."

"I am lost."

"I feel empty."

"What is the point of my life?"

These thoughts are created in the mind when your true path has been ignored, locked away or suppressed, and the heart is unbalanced. As children, we all knew what we wanted to be. This is because a child knows why their soul chose their body. A child knows what their life is supposed to be and what journey they are supposed to take. However, this aspiration, or life purpose, is ripped from the child at an early age when it is told what it is *expected* to be, and the fire in the heart slowly goes out as the soul weakens.

Following the yogic route supports the rediscovery of your purpose for being and gives you strength to redirect your life to the real reason you are here on this earth. Your Dharma – your purpose.

"Dharma is not what you do,

Not what you should do,

Not even what you want to do.

Dharma is what you were born to do"

Adil Palkhivala – The Fire of Love

Finding your Dharma

Once you have physical health, emotional balance and mental stability, your mind will begin to open to all the wonderful opportunities of living. You will find yourself no longer saying *no* to new opportunities because of old, fear-driven habits. Instead you will want to say *yes* as your mind becomes open to soul-expanding knowledge, understanding and experiences. Then, you will begin to ask your Heart:

"What is my unique mission in this life?"

"Why did my soul choose this body for this mission?"

Following a yogic way of life will help you to answer these questions as you begin to open your heart to new experiences.

Each experience, whether you enjoy it or not, is a life lesson to be used positively, and will lead you closer to your inner peace. How do you know if something makes you happy until you try it? And if it doesn't, it may open a door to something that will. So, use the gift of adrenaline positively to support the stepping forward into new situations. Go to new places, speak to new people – you never know, the next person you say hello to may change your life!

Yogic philosophy embeds the knowledge that every person you meet has a purpose in your life journey, as you do in theirs. Whether it's with a family member you've known from birth, or a total stranger just saying "hello!" as they pass by, you are connecting, you are observing, and you are learning.

When you are living in the present moment and observing what is truly happening, you see life with clarity and you see people as the unique individuals that they are. In doing this, you will then be able to learn from each person to enhance your life experience *and* teach them to enhance theirs. Everyone in your life is there for a reason: to help you grow and for you to help them grow.

Food for thought:

The person you pass by in the street may have no one. By smiling and saying hello, you may be the only person they connect with that day, you may just lift their mood enough to see them through to tomorrow. You have impacted positively on someone's life.

Be the Good Samaritan and remember that to be kind costs nothing but brings great rewards.

Exploring your Dharma is the process of going within yourself to find your true purpose.

As you prepare for a meditation practice, ask yourself the following:

"If I had all the money I ever needed, all the time and energy I desired, what would I be doing with my life?"

Answer:

Before your next practice, ask yourself the following:

"What reason do I have for not currently moving forward with that life right now?"

Answer:

Consider this:

If you were dying right now, what would be your regrets?

188

What were the dreams that you never attempted to fulfil?

Now ask yourself:

Why are you not doing these things now?

Are *you* the only thing stopping you from doing these things?

Are you waiting for some catastrophe to happen before you start listening to your heart?

Begin to gently ask yourself, is this my true choice or is it my conditioning? Start to break away from that which has stunted your way of living by exploring options and possibilities, and then try them out. The more things you try, the more you will discover your true self and understand that new experiences and learning are what we are here for. Through these explorations, you will begin to naturally connect with your inner truth and understand your true purpose. Discovering your Dharma is becoming more of the real you.

Once you have achieved your peace and understand what makes you wonderful and unique, you can then take this peace and understanding forward into every part of your life, being truthful and honest to yourself and to the world. By doing so you are *fulfilling your Dharma.*

I have discovered my Dharma, my purpose for being, the thing that my soul is here to achieve and the one thing that brings me ultimate joy. My Dharma is to support others in their path to happiness. To be a teacher, a guide, was my goal as a young soul.

I realise now that the traditional or expected pathways to 'success', which I regretted not taking when I was younger, were simply not my right path. Instead, I was supposed to experience all the knocks and bruises my life has thrown at me and work out how to come back from them and to be a better person. Yoga came into my life when I needed it the most. Yoga has made me a better person. Yoga has made me the person I am today.

My life has offered me knowledge to help me move towards my true purpose, to support others in their yoga and life. I use my experiences to try to help others understand theirs, and as a consequence, I have also healed myself on the way. This is Karma at its best

I tell you this out of love and support for your journey and to give you hope in the knowledge that your Dharma will reveal itself to you, in its own time, when you create the correct environment for it to grow.

So, in order to become your best self, nurture yourself and the people around you, invest in your true Heart and respect and develop your personal knowledge and experiences every day. Become whole and well-rounded. Then, when you share your findings and experiences, you too will experience the truest joy of living.

Good luck.

Namaste

'I do not need to pretend that I am anyone other than myself

I do not need to feel insecure about my perceptions

The Self-cultivation that I undertake is to perfect who I am

Not to become someone other than who I am'

The True Self

by Deng Ming-Dao